GHOSTS

THE BUTTON HOUSE ARCHIVES

WRITTEN BY

Mathew Baynton

Simon Farnaby

Martha Howe-Douglas

Jim Howick

Laurence Rickard

Ben Willbond

BLOOMSBURY PUBLISHING

LONDON · OXFORD · NEW YORK · NEW DELHI · SYDNEY

"Like ripples in that pond would he
  Still echo thro' eternity?
  Or ne'er again would this world see
  The idle stone she tossed . . ."

from 'Hermione and Roger'
by Thomas Thorne
(unpublished)

For those poor souls who, across the centuries, have died at Button House – or on the land it now occupies – every passing year sees the memories of them fade further; their legacies lost to time.

But before their deaths came their lives – some exceptional, others mundane; some flush with privilege, others marked only by hardship. Yet all with one thing in common: that, out there somewhere, languishing in filing cabinets and libraries, damp basements and dusty boxes, were fragments of evidence that spoke of the unique lives they led.

Collected here, for the very first time, are these arcane artefacts, rare documents and rediscovered diaries which, combined with the testimony gathered by Alison Cooper (thanks to her most unique of gifts), paint a vivid picture of the lives once lived by the restless spirits of Button House.

The Ghosts brought back to life . . .

Given that they're ghosts, they seem to know very little about how haunting works. But

GHOSTS RULES these seem to be the rules, as far as I can work out from speaking to them.

* CAN WALK THROUGH WALLS
— and do so <u>constantly</u>
(bathrooms + bedrooms seem to be a favourite) Have stopped telling Mike as he started showering in trunks
— asked why they don't fall through the ceiling when walking on first floor. 'No idea'

* CAN'T LEAVE ???might
They can't go past the) be different
edge of the grounds. ← borders for different ones? Will ask.

* STAY HOW THEY DIED
— one has no trousers on because he died like that (vague about details)
— one has an arrow in his neck — he says if he took it out it would just go back in... Sort of want to see that, but seems rude to ask.
— one has head cut off, presumably executed. Not sure which bit is weirder, head or body.

Lady B saw → actually only one
what I wrote and of them seems to
that became a whole big thing be old so maybe

* HAPPENS AT RANDOM
— None of them have a clue why they're here.
— Doesn't seem to be 'unfinished business' or 'needing to send a message' or anything.
— Violent deaths? (some of them don't seem
— Maybe it's just pot luck? to fit the bill for that)

it's something to do with going too soon???

3am thought ↙ * CAN WEE - they say it turns to
They're constantly dust. Might be having me on. What
re-weeing their are they weeing f they can't drink?
last * CAN'T AGE Once saw kitty vomit and it
drink!! disappeared. What was that?
Disgusting. - though mostly still keen to Maybe whatever
celebrate birthdays was in her tummy
when she died?
NB. 'Death Days' are less celebrated, which is
fair enough, I suppose.

* CAN'T EAT
- but talk about food a LOT! it was
I suppose they just miss it. pineapple
The cave one really misses rump steak, but
doesn't call it that. Wish he would.

* CAN SLEEP
- out of habit? Certainly they're
Have obsessive about bedrooms. Will be
stopped tricky when we have guests,
putting as they'll basically be sharing.
female friends in the politician's room.

* CAN'T TOUCH ANYTHING
- except the politician (Julian)
who can touch things with his
finger (with a lot of effort)
UPDATE: Claims he developed the skill through
'sheer perseverance'. Found an old copy
of The Sun in 1997 and spent 7 years turning

* MIGHT NOT BE FOREVER? to Page 3.
- So, apparently, they could disappear into
the great beyond (or wherever) at any
moment. There's like a bright light and
they just sort of 'move on' (Mary calls
it being 'sucked off', no matter how
much I ask her not to). Again, they
have no idea why.

To the Principal Secretary
October 3rd 1575

Sir W,

Further to questions raised in respect of the operation that did resulte in the deathe of Sir Humphrey Bone, I am glad to submit a most fulsome accounte of the night in question, replete with all such detail as can be recall'd to mind.

Upon the night of September 26th, having receiv'd, from agents of your office, goodly reason and spake accounts of Catholic collusion and treasonous plot at the home of Mister Bone, a garrison was despatch'd, under my command, to a residence in the borough of Hemel. Upon our approach to the homestead, three persons — varied in both gender and tongue — were seen to exit, whom, catching sight of the closing troops, did take to the heel in such a manner as to inspire a tincture of mistrust. Giving chase, we swiftly apprehend'd the flighty shades, then turned our weight to the doors of the house, all a while robustly announcing our authority.

Aft many a mumble and afear'd whimper was heard from within, our might at last did turn the door to splinter, and entry followed apace. A search most thoro' was conducted, by all hands, but, unable to place either Bone or his spouse within, an order was given to retreat and log warrants for arrest upon sight.

However, as I mov'd to exit the residence, a sound of effort caughte my ear, causing me to pause upon the threshold. Returning with haste to the dining room, accompanied by Sergeant Hutchens, a figure was observ'd to climbe from the breaste of the chimney, matching the suspect in given stature and the pure twin of his sketche.

Catching sight of Hutchens and I, he did produce, from the copious folds of his cloake, a broadsword, mace, hatchet and dagger, and, with a cry of "deathe to the Queen!" did lunge with greate force towards Sergeant Hutchens, across whose body I dove to deflecte the flurry of experte blows. Wrenching my own sword free of its scabbard, I manag'd to fend off his every strike, bringing the full fury of his attack upon myself. Fuell'd by the frothing venom of his Catholic rage, he did become possess'd with the strength of several men.

Fearing only for Sergeant Hutchens, who I knew to be slight of sinew and weak of bladder, I did summon the strengthe to force back the assailante with a crook'd leg, swung high my sword and, pulling down upon it with the claspe of both hands, found trew target in the necke of the a'cursed Bone, striking his head a'twain of his body.

But, alas, such was the papal fury of the suspecte, his body did continue to put up a most fearsome defence, even now divorced of a head, fleuling its razored arsenal with such precision as no sighted man could match. And again did I, in defence of the dumbstrucke Sergeant Hutchens — his mouthe agape, throw my shoulder to the bodily portion of the assailante, sending it crashing to the flagstones, and resting my whole weight there upon until the final pulse of blood did vacate the spitting cavity.

Pulled back to full height, I did then take goodly stock of the scene — noting not only the position of both parts of Bone, but also the ornamentation knocked asunder in our Herculean tussle. My breath collected, I did help Sergeant Hutchens from the scene, and ordered his weapons be tossed into the lake, so they should not again fall into Catholic hands. Washing all blood from our sleeves, we did hurry to catch up the retreating garrison and made good our first report of the dramatic encounter.

In recognition of his rally of spirits and eager assistance once danger had passed, I would recommende Sergeant Hutchens be advanced to the rank of Ensigne. And, while I seek only God's blessing in regard to my own actions, Sergeant Hutchens has humbly requested that I be considered for the role of Lieutenant of the field, having exhibited — and here I quote — "valour and bravery unmatched in any battle my eye hath witnessed".

Your humble servant,

Sergeant Major
Arthur Pinhoe

**HERTS AND BEDS REGIMENT
BUTTON HOUSE HQ**

DAILY PHYSICAL JERKS

HQ/398-2/

DATE: 31st July 1941

IT WILL TAKE MORE THAN A STIFF UPPER LIP TO GIVE HITLER A FAT LIP!

I like to encourage the men and women here at Button House to get physical as often as possible. Don't sit around idle, go at it as often as you can! Fitness is key to winning this war, not just the wellbeing of the mind but of the body too.

Here is a pictorial guide to my PHYSICAL JERKS REGIME that takes place at 0600 hrs every morning. Attendance is not compulsory but I encourage all members of the Company to attend. I am asking Command to make this compulsory.

A. 1-MILE RUN. Nothing warms the blood more in the morning than a good pump in the woods.

B. THE STAR BURST From a small crouch detonate yourself into a star shape. Do this TWENTY times.

C. THE REACH AROUND From a neutral position REACH AROUND each side of your body. You need to do this TWENTY TIMES each side.

D. TAKE COVER Sprint twenty feet then TAKE COVER! Repeat TEN times.

E. BEAT THEM OFF Jab, jab, left hook, upper cut, knock out! Let's give Jerry a bloody nose! Repeat TWENTY TIMES both arms.

F. GOD SAVE THE KING! Take a moment to reflect, get your breath back and think of God, England, and the King.

With sincere thanks to our resident artist Lt Heanley for so vividly capturing my every jerk.

University of Thame St Luke's
Department of Archaeology

ARCHAEOLOGICAL REPORT
(ABRIDGED)
BUTTON HOUSE / Site ref: HJH7865

Location

The dig is located in the basement of a dilapidated manor house in a generally poor state of repair. Late 15th-century wood-framed core, extensively remodelled circa 1650, but with documentary evidence of settlement on the site from the 12th century.

Grounds for excavation

Structural surveys, commissioned by a hotel chain, unearthed possible human remains in the immediate substrata. Initial forensic analysis confirmed the finds to be pre-Victorian, falling under the purview of History England, who commissioned excavation(s) and a site report.

Findings (abstract)

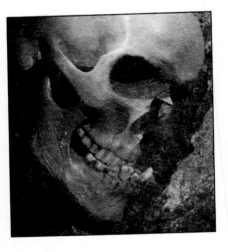

A total of 17 bodies (majority complete skeletal remains) were uncovered within the area approved for excavation, with partial remains at the trench borders suggesting a larger grave area extending beyond the foundations of the house. Core sample results have now confirmed the presence of *Yersinia Pestis* bacterium, which suggests mass infection of bubonic plague, explaining the hurried and communal nature of the grave. Carbon dating places the burial date at approximately 1345–1350, which would fit with the known prevalence of 'Black Death' in major English cities at this time.

How and why such a major outbreak of plague occurred in such a rural location is uncertain (this is only the second site of this type to be found outside of London). With travel to the capital atypical for residents of such a remote hamlet at this time, we can only hypothesise about the route by which plague came to be so prevalent in the local population.

Given the evidence discovered of pelts and fabrics within the grave site, of a quality unusual for home-woven garments, it is possible that a number of textiles were brought to the village from London by someone unaware that they were harbouring plague-bearing ticks. If said textiles were then distributed throughout the village, that may explain the blanket nature (so to speak) of infection here.

Alternatively, perhaps the hamlet was of a large enough scale to warrant an incumbent local official; someone of sufficient standing to warrant the long, arduous commute to the capital for diplomatic business, returning with an infection that then spread amongst the community.

Students from our post-graduate forensic department kindly agreed to undertake facial reconstruction based on the most complete skull found on site. Named by the department as 'Button Bill', might this be the face of the important local official whose vital business saw him bring plague to this blighted parish?

Site ref: **HJH7865**

HOUSE OF COMMONS

Unrevised transcript of evidence taken before

The Members' Allowances Select Committee

Inquiry on

FRAUDULENT EXPENSE CLAIMS RELATING TO

THE EXECUTION OF MINISTERIAL BUSINESS

Evidence Session No. 4 | Heard in Private | Questions 174 — 181

FRIDAY 19 JUNE 1992

3:30pm

Witnesses: Mr Julian Fawcett MP

CHAIRMAN: Welcome, Mr Fawcett. Thank you for sparing the time to join us today.

JULIAN FAWCETT: I was told I had to.

CHAIRMAN: You do.

JULIAN FAWCETT: Well then.

CHAIRMAN: We just have to declare any interests before we start.

JULIAN FAWCETT: Oh, well ehm... Wine, I suppose - fine wines. And rugby. Harlequins mainly, but--

CHAIRMAN: No, no. I mean any personal or business interests that might colour your testimony to the committee.

JULIAN FAWCETT: Oh, right... Would I need to say if I slept with your secretary at a party conference in '89?

CHAIRMAN: No.

JULIAN FAWCETT: Right. Good... Because I didn't.

LADY CALDER: So, Mr Fawcett, this swimming pool--

JULIAN FAWCETT: The Community Pool, yes.

LADY CALDER: Well, let's just refer to it as the swimming pool--

JULIAN FAWCETT: It's a Community Pool.

LADY CALDER: But built in your garden.

JULIAN FAWCETT: I donated a portion of my grounds to the project, if that's what you mean.

(Q174) LADY CALDER: But the cost of construction was filed as a business expense through your constituency office, is that correct?

JULIAN FAWCETT: Yes, well, it's very much a community resource, you see. Free to use for anyone living within a two mile radius of the house.

(Q175) LADY CALDER: And how many other properties are there within a two mile radius of your estate?

JULIAN FAWCETT: Well, I wouldn't know off the top of my head. I'd need to gather relevant census data to provide an accurate--

LADY CALDER: Three.

JULIAN FAWCETT: Well, if you have the answer, why ask the question?

LADY CALDER: Three houses. All of which already have their own swimming pools.

JULIAN FAWCETT: Yes, but not Community Pools.

(Q176) LADY CALDER: Mr Fawcett, if there is no community for the pool to serve, how is it a Community Pool?

JULIAN FAWCETT: If a tree falls in a forest and there's no one around, does it make a sound?

LADY CALDER: What?

JULIAN FAWCETT: Precisely.

CHAIRMAN: Mr Fawcett--

JULIAN FAWCETT: Look, we had all this out when the pool opened. That's why I expanded the catchment area to include affiliate membership for the entire village of Lower Hazeley.

LADY CALDER: Yes, subject to what you describe as 'selective membership screening'.

JULIAN FAWCETT: It is perfectly reasonable to require some personal details from prospective patrons for security reasons.

(Q177) LADY CALDER: And what were the personal details you requested?

JULIAN FAWCETT: I don't recall.

(Q178) LADY CALDER: Was it a recent photograph and vital statistics?

JULIAN FAWCETT: Look, if you have the answers there, why ask the question?

(Q179) LADY CALDER: And how many affiliate membership passes were issued as a result of this process?

JULIAN FAWCETT: Do you have the answer written down?

LADY CALDER: Yes.

JULIAN FAWCETT: Eleven?

LADY CALDER: Thirteen.

JULIAN FAWCETT: Oh, well, even better then.

LADY CALDER: All of whom are women between the ages of 18 and 27.

JULIAN FAWCETT: That's a lie! One wasn't quite-- Actually, no; carry on.

LADY CALDER: Mr Fawcett. I put it to you that the financing of this swimming pool, reimbursed - as it was - from the public purse, is a flagrant abuse of members' privilege. The pool in question is quite clearly of benefit to you alone and merely masquerades as a public resource.

JULIAN FAWCETT: Well, there's a woman in it right now who'd beg to differ.

(Q180) LADY CALDER: A single woman?

JULIAN FAWCETT: Yes, they're all single.

(Q181) LADY CALDER: No, I mean one woman? Hardly a bustling local amenity, is it?

JULIAN FAWCETT: Well Topless Friday's always quiet.

LADY CALDER: What?!

JULIAN FAWCETT: I said, 'Friday's always quiet'. No further questions.

CHAIRMAN: I say that!

JULIAN FAWCETT: Oh yes... Were you about to?

CHAIRMAN: No.

JULIAN FAWCETT: Oh... Could you?

So, this way to win any game.
Foolproof. People think chess
hard, but it not — people just
stupid. Now, might get bit
tellycall (technical?) so put it
down EXACT. OK?

OK, Good. So first...
Prawn two go dooka. So Julian do
prawn fight dooka. Dooka-dooka.
I do middle prawn, dooka, which
mean his out-prawn do takey-jump.
BUT, when his prawn dooka my
prawn, weird-willy-guy go slide
to dooka. 'Ha' he think and
dooka prawn here, here, here.
But who dis? Other-willy-guy!
Take Julian bully-prawn DOOKA!
'So what?' he think as he take lots
prawn and I do just one.
But while he deep in prawn dooka,
out go lady-hat in double-dooka.
Then just dooka-dooka, SLIDE-dooka,
CHECKMATE!
I mean, not pretty, but get
job done.

Read that back. Good. Now hide!
Show only me. Chess world see
that, it finished.

26th Jan - Written down verbatim for Robin, so he 'not forget'.
(after quite a long conversation about the word 'verbatim')
NB. Let the record show it is 5.21 am.
Says he'll let me sleep once I've 'done job'!
If he wasn't dead, I would kill him!

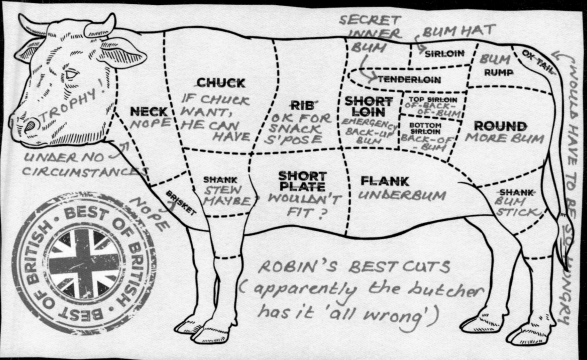

MILKING WITH MARY

Milking a cow is nots as easy as many do think.

If she be troubled, uneasy or afraid, she will not milk. Step to her slowly, speak or sing softly to her. Something's like, "Good, lovely cow, thank you for your milk."

Do not move sudden or she may run or worse, kick. Old Godfrey once was kicked by his cow, rights in the private place, and t'was never the same.

Tie her about the neck to the milking post and give her good hay to feast on. Tie her tail to her leg so it dangles not at the udders.

Sit yourself upon your stool, straights and comfy.

Next, clean the udders with good water from the stream, not the puddle. If it can be warmed from the fire, she will like it better.

Do not place the pail neath the teat for the first pulls. Firmly but gently pull the teat to get the muck out. The first pulls may be beige and lumpen, which you do not want. Do this for each teat. When it is nice and clean milk, you can puts the pail between your legs.

Take a pairs of teat in hand between thumb and first finger, so that the teat fills your palm as you squeeze. If she need encouragings, you may bump the udder as the calf would to help the milks come. Do not yank or tug, be gentle but firm and go until the udder looks no longer bulging. Make sure the hay be plenty while the milking be done.

Enjoy the milk fresh, or make butter, or whatever you likes, Al'son.

Bob-a-job-gob

by TOBY CHAMBERS

"Bloody stupid" - Boys Adventure Club Leader, Pat Butcher

A LOCAL nursing-home manager was left incensed last week after a Boys Adventure Club's 'Good Deed Day' ended in chaos.

Reading 4th group were assisting staff at the St Martin's Rest Home to raise money for local charities – an opportunity for the Young Adventurers to earn their 'Helping Hands' badge.

Linda Lineker, owner and manager of the rest home, said, "I've seen them helping people in the town over the last few years, washing cars and planting flowers. They seemed like nice lads and it was for a good cause so I thought I'd invite them to the home to help out."

"One of the boys was asked by a resident if he would sterilise his false teeth and, well, before long the idea spread and everyone wanted their dentures cleaned!" Pat Butcher, the Adventure Club's leader, explained. "Now, because there were quite a lot of teeth and the boys and I were keen to get back for The Krypton Factor semi-final, I thought, to save time, why not put them in one big bowl and wash them all together? I never considered that we'd have to put them back in the right mouths and that, I'll admit, was bloody stupid, mate."

After their initial horror, Mr Butcher and the boys set about finding the correct teeth for each resident. "At first it was tricky, matching gums with dentures, but after a while it actually became great fun!" he mused. "We missed The Krypton Factor but it didn't matter. This was OUR Krypton Factor and we completed the task in just under four hours, five minutes!"

Mrs Lineker didn't share Mr Butcher's enthusiasm. "It was a disaster. It took ages! Some teeth were too big, others too small. One poor resident already had the hair of Ken Dodd and then found himself with the teeth of Ken Dodd. And he hates Ken Dodd. It was very upsetting."

Sadly, one resident passed away while the mix-up was being rectified, though Mrs Lineker assured our reporter that the correct dentures were "swapped in" prior to the funeral.

Mr Butcher has since apologised to Mrs Lineker for the incident. "We were trying to do some good deeds, but sometimes things get taken the wrong way. Rest assured, from now on I'll be keeping my boys out of pensioners' mouths."

News

Choc shock at bird of prey display!

by COLIN TAYLOR

AN INQUIRY into the safety of wildlife entertainment is being considered by Berkshire County Council after an incident at a bird of prey display in Reading last week.

The Reading 4th Boys Adventure Club was hosting a demonstration from Big Peckers Falconry at their clubhouse and grounds, when a large bird attacked a boy in the audience.

Adventure Club leader Pat Butcher, who organised the event, said he'd never seen anything like it and was relieved that no one was seriously harmed.

"One of my lads opened a finger of Fudge at the wrong time and the condor went straight at him. Perhaps he thought it was a worm? Or maybe he's got a sweet beak?"

Originating from North America, the condor is one of the largest birds of prey in the world. With a wingspan of up to 3.2 metres and the biggest bird in the display group's collection, the condor is typically saved as the finale of the show.

"Tip to tip he's the size of Jaws from James Bond. Or half the size of Jaws from Jaws. A bloody big bugger."

Pat Butcher (left) poses with golden eagle, Apollo, prior to the incident.

Mr Butcher explained. "We'd just seen the black crows and the eagles and now it was time for the condor. He hopped out of the hutch, heard the rustle of the packaging and locked onto the boy. He galloped towards the lad like a crazed hunchback, not paying a blind bit of notice to the instructor's commands. He didn't want a dead rodent, he wanted creamy fudge, covered in Cadbury's milk chocolate."

Robert Hargreaves, nine, tried to escape but the giant bird gave chase.

"They were charging around for a good minute but Robert was still clutching his finger of Fudge," Mr Butcher continues. "'Drop the Fudge, Robert! It wants the Fudge, Robert!!' we screamed, as his cries of 'Get Mum!' resounded across the field."

Having been cornered by the bird, Robert finally threw the confectionery away and dived for cover into a nearby bramble hedge.

"Robert was very brave. He had some cuts and bruises but that provided an excellent opportunity for the other lads to practise their first-aid skills. He was patched up in no time."

Mr Butcher says he's cancelling the upcoming visit from the local snake handler "to be on the safe side" and says he'll focus the boys' activities away from the animal kingdom and on to other, safer, pursuits such as orienteering and archery.

(I have, wasn't prett

Finally yo, I wanna talk about
the attitude and spirit that equal good times,

Dearest Jane,

It is difficult to express in words what you have done to me. And I, a poet! But the language simply does not exist to describe the agonies I have suffered. My heart quickened when first I saw you and has not slowed in the days since we parted. It is as though my very thoughts are no longer my own, so completely have you captivated me. I am your prisoner. From the moment first I rise to the sound of lark (And how its song seems to tease me! Does the lark not understand that the world can hold not a shred of happiness until I am reunited with my love?) until late into the night sleep finally grants me brief respite, I see your face, I hear your voice, I remember our fingers brushing against each other as we walked about the grounds of your uncle's house. I try to drive my thoughts on to something, anything, else, but there you are. Inescapable. What sweet, bitter torture to be haunted not by a demon... but by an angel. How can you, a creature of such unbound loveliness, be the source of such unendurable pain? How may I be released? I dream of a simple kiss that, if granted, would transform this pain

to unimaginable ecstasy. And yet I fear that
a kiss from you would set my very bones on fire,
or else send me soaring into the skies on the wings
of an angel. Tell me that you think of me too.
Tell me that you ache as I do. Tell me that you
long to see me. Tell me that we shall meet
again and I shall hear once more your soft,
sweet voice.

Until then I am your servant, your slave,
   your sweetheart.

   Thomas Thorne

Dear Mr Thorne
   I am afraid I cannot recall meeting you. I
presume you refer to the weekend at Barnham
House and my Uncle Joseph? There were so
many guests present that I am afraid I do
not remember every man to whom I was
introduced. I am sorry that I have inspired
such feelings but I can assure you it was
quite without intent on my part since I am
betrothed these last four months.
   I hope that you feel better soon.
   Yours, Miss Jane Ash.

LADY BUTTON

WELCOMES YOU TO

DINNER

TO CELEBRATE

THE 50TH BIRTHDAY

OF

LORD BUTTON

MAY 17TH 1906

Button House,
Hemel Hempstead

MENU
To be Served at 8pm Sharp

First Course - Hors D'oeuvres
Turtle Mousseline and Smelts in Dutch Sauce

Second Course - Soup
Oxblood and Liquorice Consommé with a Plum Wisp

Third Course - Fish
Salmon Canterbury served with an Oyster Recollection

Fourth Course - Entrées
Lamb Groin with a Kidney Philip and a Gallop of Young Peas

Fifth Course - Removes
Dishes are changed

Sixth Course - Sorbet
Egg and Melon Fingers

Seventh Course - Game
Jellied Tongue of Partridge with a Cauliflower Cacophony

Eighth Course - Roast
A Chaud-froid of Woodcock with an Interlope of Carrots
and a Dappled Cream Removal

Ninth Course - Salad
Bruised Asparagus on a Nest of Wet Marjoram

Tenth Course - Sweets
Fanny's Flan Fanfare / Creamed Ice /
Dunwoody Pudding with a Pomegranate Spill

Eleventh Course - Fruit
Orange à l'Orange

Twelfth Course - Cheese
The Four Cheeses

"Why would you
want to kill time?
It's there to be
enjoyed, not killed!"

KITTY

NAME KITTY

WHERE WERE YOU BORN?

And you'll just write down whatever I say, exactly as I say it? Oh, you're doing it! Ha! You even wrote down, 'Oh you're doing it.' And then me saying that. And that! This is such fun! Pineapples! You wrote it down. This is the best game ever. What was the question again?

The British colony of Jamaica. It was one of my father's trade routes.

HOW DID YOU DIE?

I fell asleep.

FAVOURITE FOOD?

Certainly not egg!
I adore cake. And, even though I've never tried them, Maoams look wonderful.

A sort of 'getting to know you' exercise, as it seems like we're stuck with them.

FAVOURITE DRINK?

Switchel! A ginger punch. Very popular in my time. Eleanor used to make delicious mint tea. I should say that, just in case she's listening. Hello Eleanor!

FAVOURITE SONG?

'Don't Stop Movin'' by S Club 7... No... 'I Know Where It's At' by All Saints... No... '2 Become 1' by the Spice Girls. This is very hard. Can we do a top ten?

30

FAVOURITE SPORT?

I prefer games, such as hide-and-go-seek. And I really want to play 'spin the bottle' but no one will play with me.

BIGGEST REGRET?

Breaking the bust of my late mother.

FONDEST MEMORY?

Oh definitely playing Cinderella in the Button House Pantomime. Captain says I was made for the stage.

WORST TRAIT?

I suppose I can be a <u>smidge</u> needy at times.

ANY WORDS OF WISDOM?

Pretty much all of the Spice Girls' lyrics make you think. But if it's <u>my</u> wisdom you want... ehm... 'When handling a pineapple, wear gloves.'

T.T.

I want a hero: an uncommon <u>want</u>, *Your opening stanza is*
   full of half rhymes man!
  When every year and month sends forth a new one, *I won't pretend I*
   haven't employed a few
Till, after cloying the gazettes with <u>cant</u>, *in my own verse, but it is hardly a*
   good first impression to be
  The age discovers he is not the true one;
   trying to smuggle in
Of such as these I should not care to <u>vaunt</u>, *three past your reader before*
  I'll therefore take our ancient friend Don Juan— *you've even named your hero!*
We all have seen him, in the pantomime,
  Sent to the devil somewhat ere his time.

Vernon, the butcher Cumberland, Wolfe, Hawke, *As if he heard me, George*
   is attending to his rhyming
  Prince Ferdinand, Granby, Burgoyne, Keppel, Howe, *now, but what's this?*
Evil and good, have had their tithe of talk, *Using names! Hardly deft, sir.*
  And fill'd their sign posts then, like Wellesley now;
Each in their turn like Banquo's monarchs stalk, *If the poet is a feeble amateur,*
   Finds his rhymes most difficult,
  Followers of fame, 'nine farrow' of that sow: *Name his hero Henry Cluvieur*
France, too, had Buonaparte and Dumourier *Have him visit Mr Piffitult!*
  Recorded in the Moniteur and Courier.

<u>Barnave</u>, <u>Brissot</u>, <u>Condorcet</u>, <u>Mirabeau</u>, *We're on to you Byron!*
   Names, names, names. Not
  <u>Petion</u>, <u>Clootz</u>, <u>Danton</u>, <u>Marat</u>, <u>La Fayette</u>, *only is it cheating, it is*
   now most boring.
Were French, and famous people, as we know:
  And there were others, scarce forgotten yet, *No less than 27 names in this*
<u>Joubert</u>, <u>Hoche</u>, <u>Marceau</u>, <u>Lannes</u>, <u>Desaix</u>, <u>Moreau</u>, *first page alone! Have you no*
   pride, man?
  With many of the military set,
Exceedingly remarkable at times,
  But not at all adapted to my rhymes. *And now, he admits, there are names*
   he <u>can't</u> even rhyme. I can scarce believe people
   read this paradiddle!

I WANDERED LONELY AS A CLOUD

William Wordsworth

T.J.

I wandered <u>lonely as a cloud</u>
That floats on high o'er vales and hills,
When all at once I saw a crowd,
A host, of golden daffodils;
Beside the lake, beneath the trees,
Fluttering and dancing in the breeze.

We stumble at the first hurdle, here, since clouds rather famously come in groups. Great fleets of them, sometimes covering the whole sky. So you went for a walk and saw some flowers? How fascinating, William. Perhaps you could tell us about how green the grass is?

Continuous as the stars that shine
And twinkle on the milky way,
They stretched in never-ending line
Along the margin of a bay:
<u>Ten thousand</u> saw I at a glance,
Tossing their heads in sprightly dance.

Counted them, did you?

The waves beside them danced; but they
Out-did the sparkling waves in glee:
A poet could not but be gay,
In such a jocund company:
I gazed—and gazed—but little thought
What wealth the show to me had brought:

Is he really saying, "I saw some flowers and they made me happy?" He sounds like a child. Is he not embarrassed?

For oft, when on my couch I lie
In vacant or in pensive mood,
They flash upon that inward eye
Which is the bliss of solitude;
And then my heart with pleasure fills,
And dances with the daffodils.

Not to mention the fact that he is stretching the sentiment to four verses.

You enjoy your daffodils, William. Never mind heartbreak, violence, suffering and death! You leave those to us grown-ups!

44

33

MP Julian Fawcett teams up with Weekend Travel and the Jolly Sailor Yachting Company for an unforgettable trip around the Aeolian Islands of Sicily.

Ahoy there! For this year's summer recess, my wife Margot wanted a boutique family hotel in Gran Canaria, but how could I refuse an invitation from my favourite newspaper to undertake a seven-day sailing holiday around the collection of tiny volcanic islands just north of Sicily, especially when all the booze and food are free!

I had to call on all my powers of persuasion with Margot, but when skipper Johannes greeted us in sunny Catania with his gleaming catamaran and an open bottle of Bollinger she soon got on board both metaphorically and literally. Less impressed was our three-year-old daughter Rachel who spent the two-hour journey to Salina throwing up her Weetabix. But as the already charming Johannes said (imagine a thick South African accent), "Ah'twill do her gud, boy. Gottaget her sea legs-ah?"

When we landed in Santa Marina Salina we were greeted by a handsome maître d' called Paco who took us into his Restaurant Marina for the best twelve-course taster menu you'll ever have in your life. I adored the Flambéed Oysters, Margot loved the Chilli and Lime Mussels and little Rachel hoovered up the kids'

fish fingers in seconds. Johannes prefers his lunch a little more liquidy and sunk three bottles of Albarino (with a little help from yours truly). Wow, I've heard the expression "drink like a sailor" but Johannes takes it to a whole new level.

When we finally stumbled to the Grand Monaco Hotel in the outrageously pretty port of Pollara, Johannes took me to a local watering hole called La Botticelli while Margot took Rachel for a nap. He ordered us some tequila shots steeped in local mountain herbs, which he said we needed to "get us back dere, boy". Pretty soon I discovered what Johannes meant when he took his shirt off and started dancing on the wooden tables singing incomprehensible sea shanties. The rest of the evening was a bit of a blur and by the time I met Margot and Rachel for dinner I was stunned to discover they were serving breakfast and that it was 7.30am! Thankfully, dear Margot saw the funny side and let me have a little "sailor's nap" before we pulled up the anchor again that afternoon.

Surprisingly Johannes was as fresh as a daisy as we set sail for the famous celebrity hangout of Panerea. This tiny volcanic island really is the prettiest place outside of the Cotswold basin and Rachel was cock-a-hoop when a burly chap called

Right: Julian Fawcett ready for adventure aboard the *Uomo a Mare*.

NOT SO PL

IN SAILING

Alfonso picked us up at the harbour in his donkey taxi (there are no cars on Panerea) and let her have a go on the reins.

Whilst Margot took the little one to the pharmacy for some antihistamine pills (turns out Rachel is allergic to equines, and blew up like one of the local giant tomatoes), Johannes took me to the Hotel Reya and checked us in. The beautiful Hotel Reya boasts a who's who of patrons ranging from Peter Sellers and Ursula Andress to Julia Roberts and Emilio Estevez. Sure enough, we'd been sat at the pool bar not five minutes when actor and singer Dennis Waterman rocked up.

I hadn't met the Minder actor before but Johannes seemed to know him like a brother and it wasn't long before they were plying me with a local beverage made from the nearby bougainvillea and vodka. It turns out Dennis is a solid Conservative voter, scratch golfer and *quite* the character. He had us in stitches with a story about being stuck in a lift with General Pinochet in Selfridges and another tale about a certain female Blue Peter presenter that would make Peter Stringfellow blush. Sadly, when Margot and Rachel (now reduced to just a cherry tomato) joined us for dinner they didn't share our affection for the red-headed cockney thespian. Hardly surprising though, as he was three sheets to the wind by then and turned the air as blue as a Tory campaign bus with his off-colour jokes!

The next day, (after a couple of stomach settling Alka-seltzers) we set sail for the world's most active volcano: Stromboli. Unfortunately, Margot thought the island might be a little dangerous for Rachel and so, after a long and very civilised conversation in the bow of the catamaran, Margot decided that she would fly herself and the little one straight home at the earliest opportunity. Once this rather unexpected, but totally sensible, decision was made, Johannes – bless him – pulled out all the stops to see that my wife and child were swiftly carried to Catania and flown back to Heathrow.

Without my dear family, the visit to Stromboli had a black cloud hanging over it, and not just because it had an actual black cloud hanging over it due to the constant eruption of volcanic ash. Things are never bleak for long when Johannes is around though, and I soon cheered up when he told me to meet him at the heavenly Leopard restaurant at Ginostra, where he greeted me with yet ANOTHER celebrity friend of his, none other than Formula 1 driver James Hunt!

The 1976 world champion is quite the tease and over a lovely lobster lunch he mercilessly ribbed me about my various troubles with parliamentary committees. "Are you going to bung that

Above: When in (near) Rome . . . Julian enjoying the onboard facilities.

Above: The Sicilian coastline is replete with wonders, as well as some unremarkable rocks.
Right: 'Oh, I'm used to dealing with blinkered locals,' quipped the MP.

on expenses!?" he'd shout to the whole bar every time I ordered a drink, getting big laughs. (Ironically the drinks were on expenses, but courtesy of Weekend Travel and not the great British taxpayer.)

The last laugh was on Hunty however! When James cajoled the entire restaurant out onto the black-sanded beach for an impromptu game of cricket, a very sloshed Johannes bowled him a yorker straight onto the bridge of his nose, shattering it! If he'd been wearing his Kevlar racing helmet he'd have been fine, but sadly he was only wearing a pair of tight, white Speedos, which now looked like a butcher's handkerchief. Johannes was howling with laughter as poor James had to be airlifted by helicopter to reset his fractured snout. Sadly he missed commentating on Nigel Mansell's win in Germany the following weekend, which is a shame, but great japes!

On our final day we visited the stunning

shops and boutiques of Lipari where I bought so many gifts for Margot and Rachel that Johannes joked, "We're gonna need a bigger boat, boy!" A hilarious reference to one of my favorite films, Steven Spielberg's Jaws, but instead of a massive shark, he was talking about my shopping bags! I don't know about a bigger boat, but I certainly need a new liver after

one last night with Johannes! To cut a long story short we ended up hosting an after-hours party on the catamaran involving the Aeolian netball team and a brass band. Needless to say, I can still hear said brass band ringing in my ears as I write these words safely back in the Bramptons in the arms of my family. (Well, almost, Margot and Rach have gone for a perfectly routine few days with her mother.)

It had its ups and downs but all in all I can highly recommend The Jolly Sailor Yachting Company experience. The beds are comfy, the bar is always full and I can guarantee a fantastic time for all the family providing they stay the full trip. Book now for the experience of a lifetime!

Just a last note, don't try and book Johannes as skipper as shortly after our trip the JSYC relieved him of his services (he's now doing security work in Kuwait). JSYC stress however, that they have plenty more able skippers who display a less "hands on" approach to their clients' holidays. So, what are you waiting for? Hoist up the mast and anchor and get sailing! Land ahoy!

Portrait (damaged) thought to be
of Sir Humphrey Bone (1531–1575).
Artist unknown. Extensive water
damage to upper canvas.

Statue (damaged) of Sir Humphrey Bone (1531-1575). Sculptor unknown. Head section missing, presumed lost.

120

Rap instead of an introductory speech?
More interesting/fun. Must be cool!

Summer Camp Rap!!!

Yo Everybody! How do you do?
My name's Lil P and I'm here to tell you,
the rules and regulations
Rules and obligations
That'll make this Summer Camp
safe and fun, it's true!

First we gonna talk 'bout general hygiene!
It's really so important to keep yo'self clean
One lad I knew didn't wash for a week,
He ended up with worms in his cheek.

(Basically a fungal infection in his mouth)

Second up, it's fire safety,
It's highly dangerous, so listen closely,
When the fire's burning, don't muck about,
Keep your distance, if in doubt,
A boy in my group once got too close,
His shell suit went up like a hot piece of toast
(Lost all his hair and an eye, y'all!)

33

them
lled
t mad
d so
tched
ruit
e
crabs
One
nose,
horts,
found
ssed
t in
ey did).
h and
ea,

aded
he lads
ocket
2p
e won 20
ne. (Mr
mally
ear old
e but 20
nd it's
the lad
. No one

he
ok in a
Flanagan.
carefully
lines.
r a true

Fri Dec 23rd.............
CAROLS BY CANDLELIGHT
(not by candlelight)

gone for
tottered back with a load of pork

companion' and warned me of a
'great pain in the neck'.

Third is a word on relationships,
Boundaries and practice of common kinships
Stay out of the girl's camp after dark,
If I catch you sneaking in, you'll hear me 'bark!
On my very first camp a boy disobeyed me
Was a kissin' and cuddlin' with some little lady,
Carried on for a week cos they were love crazy,
And she ended up having his baby!

(They're 26 now. Still together and very happy.
Live in Plymouth.)

Fourth of course is the litter rules,
Use a bin, don't be a fool
Dropping litter is rude and ~~xxxx~~ foul,
Ever seen a bag of crisps strangulate an Owl?

(I have. Wasn't pretty.)

Finally yo, I wanna talk about the vibes,
The attitude and spirit that equal good times,

If we all work together, we'll get along just fine,
And I promise you that absolutely nobody'll die

(Someone might die, y'all)

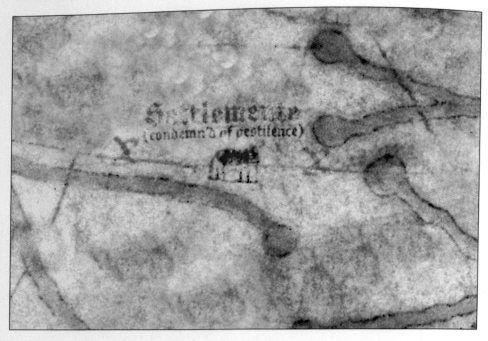

The Brownlow Map, 1354. Historical records show a hamlet on the site as early as the 12th century, though it was abandoned around 1350 following an outbreak of bubonic plague – rare for such a remote, rural location.

Bone House, circa 1457. Home to popular landowner Sir Alexander Bone, it is thought to be the first baronial house on the site.

Bone Hall, built 1501.

Bone Hall, following a disagreement with tenant farmers, 1518.

Bone Hall, rebuilt 1521 to the original design (with additional funding from the estate's tenant farmers).

Higham House, 1813. Site of the first meeting between heiress Lady Isabella Higham and philanthropist Francis Button, after whom the house was subsequently renamed. It is believed they were introduced by a mutual friend, though his identity was not recorded.

Button House, 1912. This painting was commissioned by the then mistress of the house, Lady Stephanie Button. Tragically, she did not live to see it completed, falling from an upstairs window after being surprised by a mouse.

Button House, 1968. The house briefly became an artists' retreat, home to 'The Button Collective' of 'right-leaning free-thinkers'. Their work included a semi-naked bed-in to promote tax relief for small-to-medium-sized corporate entities.

Button House today. After its moment in the spotlight, following the untimely death of MP Julian Fawcett at a political fundraiser in 1993, its future now seems uncertain. The current owner, Lady Heather Button, has no direct descendants, and often jokes, 'I may just leave it to the ghosts!'

"Who put his knickers in a Twix?"

ROBIN

NAME ROBIN

WHERE WERE YOU BORN?

Dunno.

HOW DID YOU DIE?

Bear. Well, not just bear, but bear's fault.

FAVOURITE FOOD?

Bum. Best bit of animal is bum. Well... not actual 'bum'. Bit round bum.

FAVOURITE DRINK?

River water. Puddle water more tasty, but risky business.

FAVOURITE SONG?

'Get Down Tonight' by KC and the Sunshine Band.

FAVOURITE SPORT?

Chess. Also favourite musical.

BIGGEST REGRET?

Try not have regret. Though did fall sleep when guarding tribe and pack of wolf eat quite a lot of family. So... not regret as such, but would do bit different.

FONDEST MEMORY?

Dennis Taylor beat Steve Davis in '85 World Champion.

WORST TRAIT?

Incest.

ANY WORDS OF WISDOM?

No. It take ten thousand year get this smart. I not give you shortcut.

LADY STEPHANIE BUTTON
BUTTON HOUSE
NR HEMEL HEMPSTEAD, HERTFORDSHIRE

18th May 1902

My Dearest Elspeth,

I do hope this letter finds you well. I could hardly contain my excitement when I received the invitation to join you at Knutsford next month. I should be delighted to come!

Now – I simply must share with you the latest impropriety involving Lady Tweedsmire. You won't believe it when you hear. Honestly, scandal follows that woman everywhere!

Do you remember dear Margaret Barky who lost her husband, Amos, in that unfortunate accident with a billiard ball?

Well, Margaret was invited to take tea with Lady Tweedsmire on Wednesday last, and would you believe, they took their seats in the Drawing Room and had to wait a full six minutes before the tea was served. Six! It beggars belief. The pastries arrived in good order I am told, but as the plates were stacked upon the curate it became clear to all that one leg had become marginally warped, causing the entire frame to audibly rock upon the selection of each and every sweet treat. Can you imagine the ruddy cheeks as Lady T herself had to prop the offending leg with a fold of doily? And the less said about the stalk-to-leaf ratio in the sandwich cress, the better.

How Margaret maintained her composure in the face of such a circus is beyond my comprehension. I very much hope that all the staff were handed their papers the moment poor Margaret left the building.

Talking of staff, I am delighted to say that our new gardener, Henry, has been the most rewarding discovery. George spotted him at work on the hedgerows at Leonardslee and was so intrigued by his topiary that he negotiated a transfer of deeds with Sir Edmund on the spot. He only has joined us last month, but already the gardens are greener than ever and far more bountiful of bloom. Even George, whose interest in horticulture has been historically scant at best, has developed a keen interest in Henry's toil—and this despite his debilitating hayfever, poor mite. Every afternoon, he comes back inside with his eyes red and steaming from the pollen as he's taken to sitting under the arbour, sometimes for over an hour, watching Henry work! I've told him it's not necessary to study him so closely, as he's more than proved his abilities, but George said he needs a little more convincing. Oh! And do you remember the Butler, Evans? Well, he and George are off on a little trip on Thursday. George said he fancied a walk by the sea, and of course it's only right that Evans accompanies him. I believe they're

going to Wales, which I hear is where
Evans' mother lives. I gather he has
a very close relationship with her. I
did moot the idea that I might also
like a sojourn to the coast, but
George reminded me I have my bridge
class on Friday, so I shall be staying
here to hold the fort! Not a bother,
Dante and I will keep each other
company!

I shall look forward to hearing all
your news upon receipt of this letter.

Sincerely,

Fanny

CUSTOMER *Lady Stephanie Button*

COLLEGE PLACE, LONDON

February 15th, 1903 DATE

E. Gerrard & Sons

TAXIDERMY & ANATOMICAL MODELS

Estimates given for all kinds of Taxidermy Work

		£	s	d
Small dog, Pedigree, Papillon. Male. "Dante"	As per quotation: to flay, excoriate, excarnate, wire, sculpt, mount and groom specimen to the fullest approximation of life. (Customer has requested an expression of 'high spirits tinged with docile servitude' and been advised of canine muscular constraints)	£ 2	4	6
	(Customer has requested the addition of a second testis, unmatched in scale to the incumbent)		1	10
	All brawn, chitlins and gizzards to be returned to customer for domestic interment. A vessel has been provided, to be found in the cold store, labelled "Dante — meat".		2	6
	Premier service requested: barrel stitched beneath, with all gathering stitches to be dressed into the pinch of the anus.	£ 1	2	0
	Plaque to read: "My dearest Dante, constant companion, confidante and comfort. Peerless, even amidst a shining breed. Diminutive in stature, yet statuesque in spirit. May every duck in heaven know the wrath of your yap, and every cloud the soft pad of your step"	£ 1	3	6
18 Feb	Following quotation for engraving, inscription revised to just "Dante".		2	6

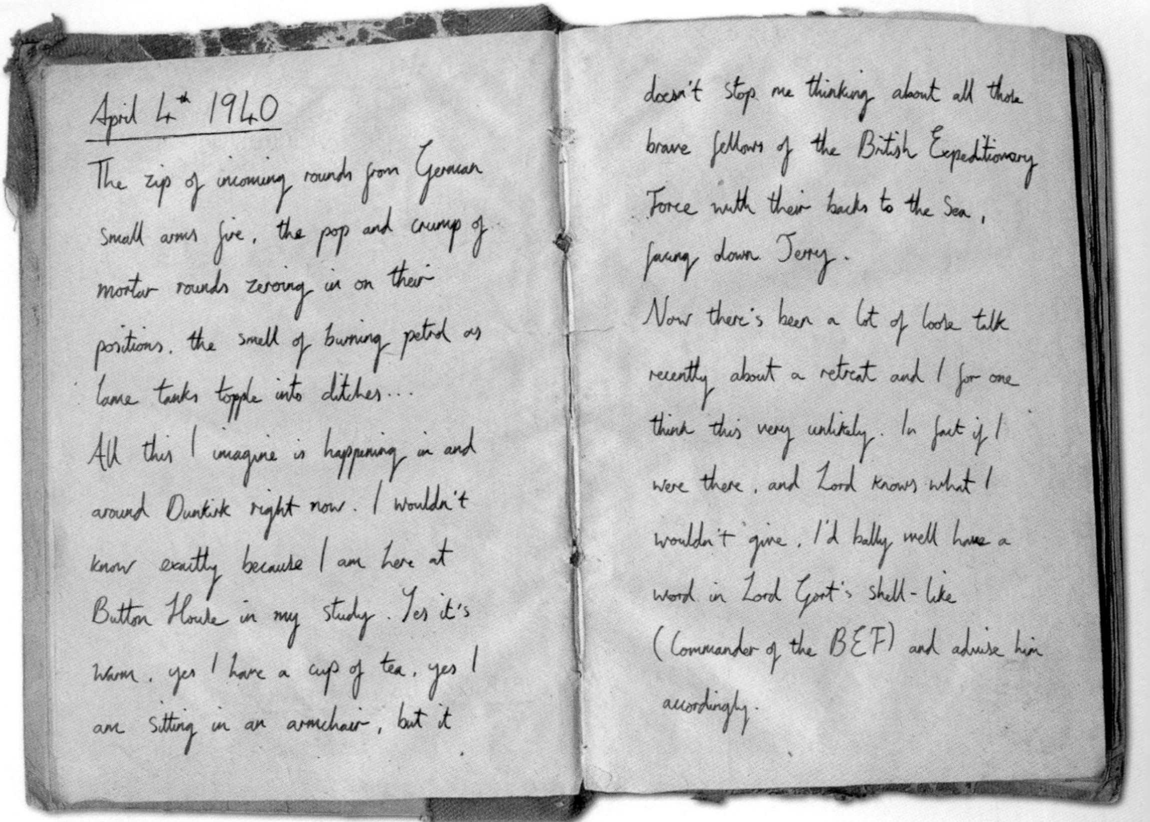

April 4th 1940

The zip of incoming rounds from German small arms fire, the pop and crump of mortar rounds zeroing in on their positions, the smell of burning petrol as lame tanks topple into ditches...

All this I imagine is happening in and around Dunkirk right now. I wouldn't know exactly because I am here at Button House in my study. Yes it's warm, yes I have a cup of tea, yes I am sitting in an armchair, but it doesn't stop me thinking about all those brave fellows of the British Expeditionary Force with their backs to the sea, facing down Jerry.

Now there's been a lot of loose talk recently about a retreat and I for one think this very unlikely. In fact if I were there, and Lord knows what I wouldn't give, I'd bally well have a word in Lord Gort's shell-like (Commander of the BEF) and advise him accordingly.

fig. 1
fig. 2

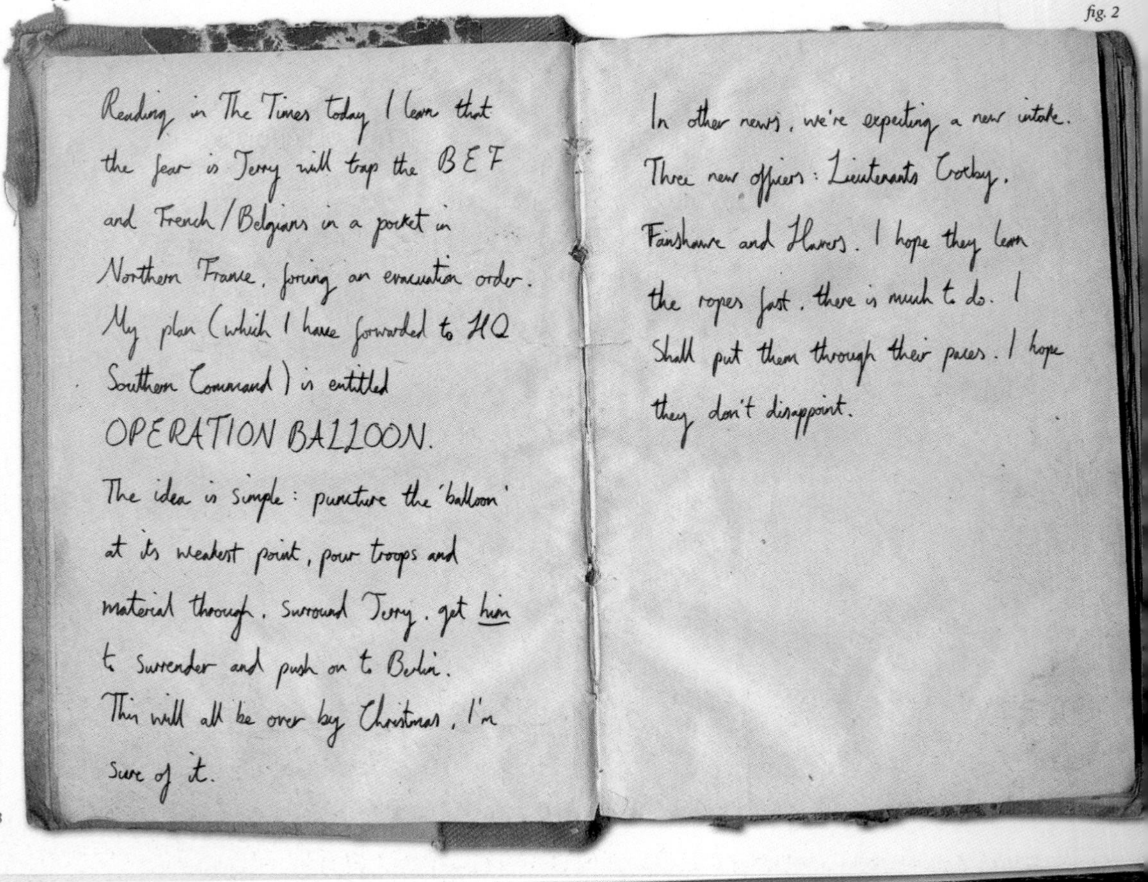

Reading in The Times today I learn that the fear is Jerry will trap the BEF and French/Belgians in a pocket in Northern France, forcing an evacuation order. My plan (which I have forwarded to HQ Southern Command) is entitled OPERATION BALLOON.

The idea is simple: puncture the 'balloon' at its weakest point, pour troops and material through, surround Jerry, get <u>him</u> to surrender and push on to Berlin.

This will all be over by Christmas, I'm sure of it.

In other news, we're expecting a new intake. Three new officers: Lieutenants Crosby, Fanshawe and Havers. I hope they learn the ropes fast, there is much to do. I shall put them through their paces. I hope they don't disappoint.

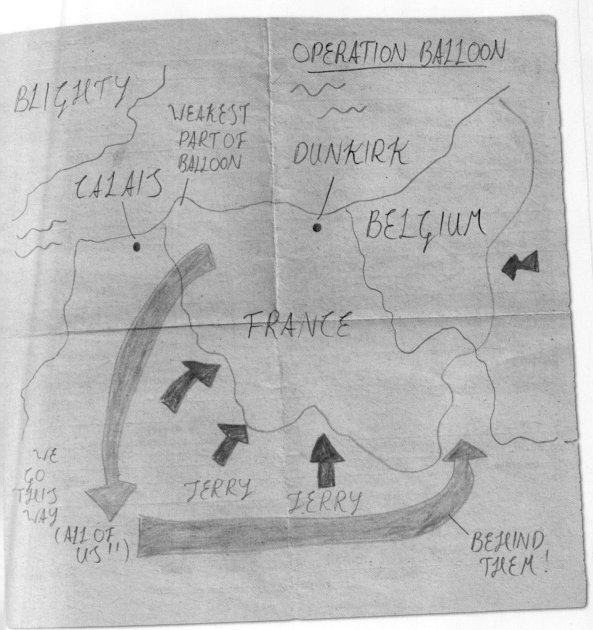

fig. 3

DISHONOURABLE

MEMBER

FAWCETT COMES UNDONE

FATA
HAMI

ALL MOUTH, NO TROUSER'S
Outspoken MP dies half naked

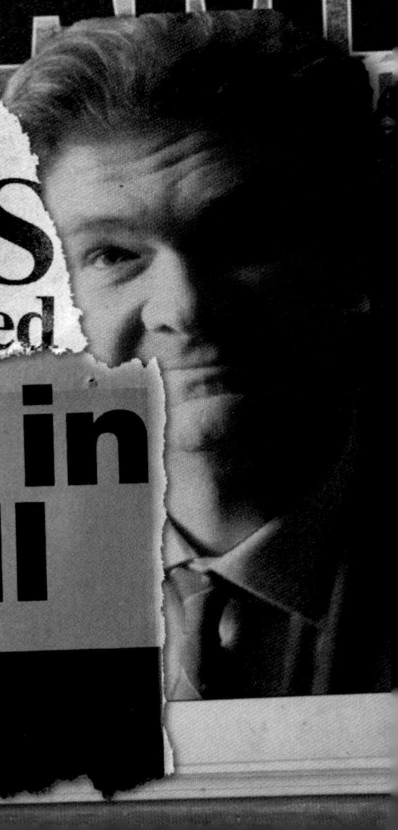

Sex & drugs in socks at poll

MP's Romp
Death At Election
Fundraiser

REST IN BRIEFS
MP dies with trousers down

£25,000
BINGO! TURN TO PAGE 13 FOR NUMBERS

NEWS

Friday, March 19, 1993   25p   DEDICATED TO THE PEOPLE OF BRITAIN

GONE, BUT TOP NO BOTTOMS
MP dies half cut and half dressed

FRIDAY, MARCH 19, 1993

30P

BELOVED MP DIES IN TRAGIC ACCIDENT

Robin and
Julian with
their game
faces on.
Chess is
a serious
business!

The boys
enjoying
another
of Pat's
favourite
matches.

Thomas
points out
his least
favourite
authors
to Mary.

Pat and
Kitty argue
over the
merits of
eggs.

REMAIN GAY

because HE wants YOU to go down!

"Good morale is the key to victory!"

Produced for the Ministry of Information

In conversation

hen it comes to polite conversation, some things are so obvious you would think they scarcely bare mentioning, and yet one encounters again and again the same terrible flaws, so point them out I must!

Do not speak too loudly. There is nothing more unseemly than a young lady speaking at the same volume as a man. As well as suggesting an indecorous strength of opinion, the increased airflow required for such forcible projection also increases the risk of 'spittle' ejection several fold. And I cannot imagine anything more uncouth than a rogue droplet landing upon the apparel of an unfortunate listener. It is said that Lady Brabham's oldest daughter once increased her volume while in conversation with a business acquaintance of her late father. As a result, a droplet of saliva landed upon the poor gentle-man's dress collar and the lady in question had to move to the Scottish Borders.

Equally, one should never speak too quietly. If your companion has to ask you to repeat yourself, it is a sure sign you are drivelling unintelligibly and the unfortunate soul cannot make out your point. You are straining their poor ears with your lazy diction. Were such a strain to cause a rupture to their eardrum, your father would be liable for their doctor's bill and the resultant scandal would see you never marry.

Never speak too much. You would not eat all the food at the table and neither should you eat all the words in a conversation. It is greedy and vulgar.

Neither should you speak too little. Your companion will presume that you find them uninteresting and dull-witted. Even if this were true (and it so often is), it would be terribly coarse manners to allow them to suspect it. A simple way to ensure the proper level of engagement is to keep a count of how many comments each person has made and be sure that your number is neither the highest nor the lowest of any of your party. Of course, if there are only two of you, make sure your score is equal unless the other party is male in which case a proper lady will make 20 to 40 percent fewer remarks than the gentleman. (So for every fifteen comments he makes, you should be making between three and six. Simple!)

Do not interrupt. Interrupting anyone who is speaking is a clear sign of ill-breeding. A truly polite lady will not speak until she has been addressed, no matter what the circumstances. If a person's hair is on fire, you may inform them when they leave a pause in which to do so. In order to appear generous in conversation, take care to compliment your interlocutor. Ideally the compliment would be truly meant but, if you can find nothing to praise in all honesty, at least choose something that you can tolerate and aren't positively disgusted by, in case you are called to expand upon your remarks. On one memorable occasion, I made the rather poor choice of complimenting young Miss Crossley's new hairstyle. Frankly it was so frightful I could think of nothing else to mention and I panicked. Fortunately, as a master conversationalist I was able to improvise several details to bolster the sense of genuine admiration, saying I thought the way it fell across her forehead was 'interestingly shapeless' and that the length around the sides and back must be 'very à la mode' when, in fact, I thought the overall effect was unkempt and utterly ghastly.

4/8/81 PART ONE
HOLA Mum and Dad! (Spanish that.)
Arrived safely after an eventful flight
Bumpy to the point of verbals and sat
in the smokers section! Still no harm
done. Weather is perfect for Carol
and Daley but too hot for this
shade-dweller keeping topped
up with suncream so I can enjoy
myself <u>and</u> watch those moles. For
tea tonight we're off to a place where
they do a superb sausage, egg and
chips and a pint of Bass for 137
pesetas! (a pound).
Hopefully postcard number 2 has
arrived so you can
read on...

FOTOGRAFIA ESPAÑOLA

© No Muy Buena Fotografía Española, Madrid

TOSSA DE MAR (Costa Brava)
Diversos aspectes

To Mr and Mrs A.P.
Butcher
22, McChesney Lane,
Almondbury
Huddersfield,
HD4 7BJ
ENGLAND

Dep. Legal: F 4563-1979

ESPAÑA
CORREOS

Tossa de Mar

Images des Tossa de Mar

COSTA BRAVA
TOSSA DE MAR
Serie 12 – Núm 654629

Part 2

(not to mention the lion
ha ha)

Hola!
After a slap-up tea we're off to an
animal-themed crazy-golf course
that Daley loves! The last hole is
a lion and you hit the ball up a
path into its mouth and it comes
out the other end! Last night Daley
went first and the ball never came
out. I reached into the lion's anus
to try and fish it out but my
watch got caught. Was stuck there
for an hour! There was an awful
back up for the golfers

See you when we get
back and we can go
through the photos, I've already
got through 6 films!

Till then,
Love,
Patrick, Carol and Daley xxx

To: Mr and Mrs A.P. Butcher,
22 McChesney Lane,
Almondbury,
Huddersfield, HD4 7SJ
ENGLAND

· Fot. en color de G. Fernandez y F. lopez

Deposito Legal B 6584-1979

Postale color Valencia Teléf. 231 11 22

Dear Jane,

You cannot recall? Are you quite sure? I hardly think it plausible that I could have mistaken what passed between us. Unless it were possible for a man to take a few polite words from a lady as ample foundation upon which to build a tower of passionate and unrequited longing! It seems absurd to imagine that our fingers brushed together by chance! Or that when you said, "I must go and speak to my cousin now," you meant anything less than, "I fear if we continue in this direction we will lose ourselves and do something scandalous right here in the gardens and, however much it pains me, I must find a distraction from these tempestuous thoughts and feelings to preserve my decorum." No, I am quite sure of the mutual nature of our feelings.

Perhaps propriety forbids you from breaking off your engagement? Perhaps even as you wrote those coldly formal words, the tears were falling down your soft, rosy cheeks. Perhaps your bosom heaved with sobs as you thought of the passionate unbridled expression of longing you could not commit to the parchment.

If only! Or perhaps your father has forbidden you to entertain romantic thoughts for any but a match he has approved?

Perhaps you are simply afraid of the heat of your passion. It is natural to stand back from a flame for fear of burning. Yes! Something prevents you from writing honestly, I am sure of it.

Do reply, sweet Jane, I implore you. Forget propriety, forget your father or whatever holds you back. To hell with the consequences!

Your devoted secret paramour,

Thomas Thorne

Dear Mr Thorne,

I really must insist that I cannot recall our meeting. Perhaps you have me mistaken. I assure you your correspondence shall not go further than me, but let us end it now and forget the whole matter.

Miss Jane Ash

4 April 1779

Today was such a perfectly fun and fabulous day
I simply had to write it down! After breakfast (plum
cake, deliciousness itself!) father had to ride to town to do
some boring business and because I asked very nicely he
said we could take the carriage so that I might visit
Grantham & Son and look at all their wonderful fabrics!
Eleanor decided that, if I was going, she simply had to
come too. Hooray! Double the fun! I thought that all
the fabrics were divine with their beautiful intricate
patterns and their brilliant colours but luckily Eleanor
was there to inform me which ones I was wrong to like
and to let me know when my tastes were unfashionable
and disgusting! When father had finished his business
he came to find us and to our great surprise, he let us
choose fabrics for a new dress each! Thankfully, I knew
not to pick my favourite one after Eleanor's generous
instruction. Instead she chose for me a very heavy
fabric in a dark burgundy which she told me is the
most fashionable colour for young ladies, even in
London! Fortunately for father, it was also one of
the cheapest! Eleanor picked for herself a shimmering
golden fabric as she said it would not be fair if
she had the same as me. How kind!

I'm going to have the happiest, fondest dreams of
the two of us in our new dresses. I'm the luckiest
girl in the world!

21 July 1779

What a day! I can swim! I absolutely had to write it down.

It all started when Eleanor decided that the weather was so beautiful that it would be criminal to stay indoors at our sewing and instead we should take a turn about the grounds. We had such a lovely time looking at the new flowers and the bees buzzing around them. Well, when we came by the lake, Eleanor said how inviting it looked and how heavenly it would be on a hot day like this to just throw away our dresses and jump in. I remarked that before I became part of the family I had never learned to swim. "Never?" asked Eleanor. "Never," I replied. And the next thing I knew, she had pushed me in! Well, I was thrashing around and gulping big mouthfuls of the lake and making a great spectacle of myself, I should say!

"Help! Help!" I screamed. "Please!" But Eleanor stayed on the jetty, laughing uproariously. "That's how you learn to swim!" she shouted. Well, I soon saw the funny side and found myself giggling away as I kicked and pulled at the water desperately trying to get moving back to the shore. I was making great splashes with my feet and hands and, sure enough, I started to move! I soon felt the ground under my feet and clambered out, soaking wet, onto the muddy bank. Once I'd been a bit sick and got the water out of my tummy, I thanked Eleanor for teaching me and even though I could tell I hadn't swum very properly she was very kind not to say a word to Papa about it when we were back inside. How lucky I am. I shall certainly dream of fishes tonight!

"Get out! Get out!
Get out! Get out!
Get out! Get out!"

MARY

NAME MARY

WHERE WERE YOU BORN?

To be's honest, I don't full remember. But my mother did say she was milkings at the teat of Herbert's goat when I did's drop, kicking and a-sprawling. Fair upset the pail she said. Sixth child of eight, so t'was humbly marked. Did'st not even stop milking she said.

HOW DID YOU DIE?

I'd rather not talk abouts that, if it be's the same to you

FAVOURITE FOOD?

Plum or pear or apple or apricot. But without a wasp in.

FAVOURITE DRINK?

The water from the river oft was mucky and the milk would not stay fresh so we mostly drank of ale made from the barley. If you drank enough it did make time go funny and the ground be like in a boat.

FAVOURITE SONG?

Can I says 'talking'?

FAVOURITE SPORT?

The menfolk of the village would play 'cudgel' whereby they woulds hit each other till one be dead. Did turn my stomach to witness. But did means few less menfolk, so...

BIGGEST REGRET?

Ooh, I'd say about nine potatoes long. Nine with the beak.

FONDEST MEMORY?

Sitting by the old oak tree with my friend Annie, casting most foul aspersions on the livings menfolk. T'was slow to train my cursing tongue, but this day I did call one a (couldn't write down)

WORST TRAIT?

I most-times am quiet, but I do have a temper if I am pushed. What be the word? Combustible. Yes. I do wish I was not combustible.

ANY WORDS OF WISDOM?

Score not trim at the root and it will hold together better in the water.

LADY STEPHANIE BUTTON

BUTTON HOUSE

NR HEMEL HEMPSTEAD, HERTFORDSHIRE

Mr J. Bruce Ismay
White Star Line
30 James Street
Liverpool

Wednesday April 24th, 1912

Regarding: Ticket Refunds

Dear Mr Ismay,

I appreciate that this must be a relatively trying time for your company, given recent events. However, I am writing to complain in the strongest possible terms about the wholly unacceptable level of service I received from your staff on April 10th, some two weeks past.

My husband and I were booked to travel via your Atlantic service on the maiden voyage of RMS 'The Titanic', but arrived at Southampton to be told that two passengers giving our names had already booked into our first-class cabin. We attempted to prove our identities to quayside stewards at the White Star office, but 'The Titanic' set sail before the veracity of our documentation could be verified to the satisfaction of your heel-dragging employees. We have since learned that the likely culprit in this duplicity was working class (an applicant for a domestic post at our estate), and should have been recognised as an imposter by your gate-line staff from her teeth alone!

Attempts to settle this matter with your London office have proved most unsatisfactory, as we were simply told that we should 'count ourselves lucky' – a reference, presumably, to our continued physical liberty and good health, which no way recognises the financial loss we have endured. Granted, there was an iceberg-related operational complication in the voyage's latter portion, but that does not detract from our contractual right to have experienced it.

Given the circumstances, we are prepared to overlook the part of the planned journey that, for understandable reasons, had to be cancelled at short notice. We do, however, expect a refund for the prior seven eighths of the voyage that progressed without incident and would have made for a most pleasant excursion, had we been party to it. We would, therefore, expect that a company cheque to the value of fifty-seven pounds, seven shillings and six pence (£57/7/6) be issued and dispatched to my husband by return of post.

Thank you in advance for your time and assistance in this matter.

Yours sincerely,

Stephanie Button.

Lady Stephanie Button
Would-be survivor/victim of the RMS 'The Titanic'

P.S. My husband, George, asked to be remembered to you. He acted as a consultant to the board re: cost-cutting measures and hopes his ideas about lifeboat provision proved beneficial.

CRICKET REPORT

The Button House XI v RAF Dunham Marsh XI

May 20th 1940

A bright, clear morning greeted us at Button House for the grudge match against our old rivals RAF Dunham Marsh. An attempt was made by those pesky fly boys to spook us early on; two Spitfires treated us to a low level mock attack at 0630 hrs. Of course I was already up and half way through some particularly strenuous morning jerks (quite surprised not to see any of the team there – the noticeboard is quite clear: 0600 hrs for Captain's Physical Jerks!!). I will say that at a distance it's jolly hard to know if an approaching plane on a strafing run is a friend or foe. Suffice to say I will be sending Group Captain Aitchison my laundry bill.

The RAF rabble started to arrive shortly after 1000 hrs. I know they have earned the right to some swagger but really, is it too much to ask for a good haircut and to tuck those shirts in!

At the toss (which I lost), Sqn Ldr Breville-Knox elected to field. A good decision given the wicket looked lively.

And so it proved. Our opener Borrowsby took a couple of rather dull overs to bed in and looked sluggish at the crease, finally swiping at a very straight, low ball from Flt Lt Daish. Heanley followed quickly, clean bowled by Sqn Ldr Carrow and our opening pair looked a sorry sight as they trudged back to our makeshift pavilion (many thanks again to the church warden Mr Farnham at St Luke's for the marquee).

But then it was Havers' innings. Brisk to the crease as ever, almost marching in, head held high and certainly not listening to any of the chit-chat coming from the outfield. He has a curious way of opening his shoulders up, twirling the bat around in a full circle, first with one arm, then the other. He turned to the RAF's keeper and quipped, "Just like one of your propellers, eh?" I laughed a lot at that!

At the other end Cpl Norriss played with a straight bat.

Then it was time for the bowlers to have a go at Havers. Good luck with that! Havers' first shot of the match was straight out of the teaching manual. A fierce front foot punch that cracked off the middle of his willow, streaking through the covers like a tracer round. The fielders had no time to react as the ball ran for four, even ploughing its way through the soggy outfield. He was off, accelerating like a sports car, and the scoreboard was ticking over.

Cpl Norriss continued at the other end.

Havers was playing without a cap at first, despite the day warming up, his sandy hair tossed about in the summer breeze like wheat as he took the bowling attack apart. Methodical, like a conductor who knows where he wants this particular piece of music to go. Two more majestic fours and a six followed in quick succession. Hot work! His jumper was off now and as Norriss trudged off for a desultory seven runs after nipping one to slip, I was able to watch the action closer as I jogged to the middle. It's easy to see how hard he hits the ball when you get a good look at his forearms. Firm and strong, like oiled oak. Crack! Another four! And how polite he is to the bowler too, smiling after each shot in a modest way, resettling himself for the next attack. A quick twizzle of the bat as he settles at the crease, like a bird of prey, (a kestrel perhaps?) on a branch. What majesty! Time itself seems to stand still when one is at the crease with Havers.

I don't know how, but I got a duck. Hinton, York and Foster never really looked like they had any fight in them but Cork showed backbone with a brisk 32. Only Fountain and Banbury were able to hold on for any time. Banbury also had a good innings, hitting a century. We set a total of 324.

Havers was not out for 88! A stunning innings and he even led the applause for their team at the end. So gracious. XXXXWe are so lucky to have him on the team.

The chase was on.

Scorecard

Button House XI Innings

Lt H.S.F Borrowsby	LBW Daish 4
2nd Lt R.J.C Heanley	Bowled Carrow 5
Cpl M.A Norriss	Caught Bright Bowled Daish 7
Lt A.P. Havers	Not Out 88
Capt.	Bowled Penton-Voak 0
Lt.	Caught Wilkins Bowled Breville-Knox 46
Lt.	Bowled Minards 32
2nd Lt.	Bowled Minards 12
Pvt. P. Banbury	Bowled Breville-Knox 108
Lt R.C. York	LBW Carrow 9
Sgt E.E. Foster	Caught Bright Bowled Daish 2
Extras:	8 wides - 4 no balls.

Out came the openers, Breville-Knox of course and Flt Lt Voles. They were
refreshed after lunch and despite our very best
the day was really

A Tale Most Heinous & True
of the foul actes committed by the
notorious Witch Mary Guppy
Apprehended in the parish
of Hemehemsted and arraigned,
condemned and executed at
Bone Hall on the 13th Daye
of Februarie laste
Anno.1612

Imprinted at London for Edward White at the little North-doore of
Paulus at the signe of the Gun, and there to be fold.

ary Guppy, widowe of John Guppy, of the age of forty and one, or thereaboute, having been apprehended was brought personally before the assize at Bone Hall.

The assize herd her, by the testimony of her honest neighbors, to be a leude, malicious and hurtful woman to the people and inhabitants thereaboutes.

Good master Owen Cheeke, of this parish saith that the said Mary Guppy was known to have used sorcerie of charms to kill her husband by means of her maleficium. That she hath taken control of his horse as a puppet master takes its doll and caused the horse to turn the plow upon him and all at once drive him into the ground crushing his bones and body until he be quite dead. By means of her devious influence, the said Mary Guppy at first convinced her honest neighbours that this was an accident.

Mrs Gwendolyn Cheeke, wife of the said Owen Cheeke, saith that Mary Guppy oft was heard to talk when no person was beside her and that it was known that this was conversation with a demon she did keep in her basket.

It was the belief of the honest neighbours that the demon was likely in the form a small animal such as a mouse, being that it fit in the basket.

The foul defendant complained that no one did ever see the mouse but the said Owen Cheeke saith that the said Mary Guppy speaking to the demon mouse was proof most obvious that the demon mouse was real and that the said Mary Guppy hath bargained with the demon mouse to bring an unseasonable frost to cause the crops to fail and bring misfortune upon the people of the parish.

Another honest neighbour saith that the said Mary Guppy did oft feed wild cats and all did agree that the said cats were likely the Devil in cat form and that the said Mary

Guppy was conspiring with them.

Then spoke a most elderly honest neighbour, one Godfrey Panke, of long beard and voice most trembling, that he hath seen himself the said Mary Guppy feed the cats with blood which she causeth to flow from her own flancke. He said also that he hath seen her to transforme herself by devilish meanes, into the shape and likeness of a toad and meet with other witches in a puddle just next to the hollybush and the honest neighbours hath all

agreece that their misfortune was caused by the Devil in the form of a cat or mouse and by Mary and the other foul toad witches.

The assize hath inspected the body of the said Mary Guppy whereupon was found a brown mark on her back which all agreede to be a mark of the Devil, with which to give suck the Devil when it come to her in the form of a mouse or cat.

The good honest neighbours have given Mary Guppy chance to prove innocence at the

ducking stool but the foul witch hath floated and the said Godfrey Panke hath cried that the witch did not only float upon the water but severale foot clear above the water moste unnaturally and all the good honest righteous neighbours hath agreede.

The assize did find the foul ugly heinous witch Mary Guppy to be guilty in three causes for witchcraft. One for murdering by sorcerie her husband John Guppy, one for conspiring with the Devil to curse the crops, and one for conspiring with other witches in a puddle in the forms of toads.

The horrible witch did shout and cry and shake her head from side to side most unnaturally and all the good honest righteous virtuous neighbours agreed it was as though the Devil himself had her body. The judgement was given that she be burnt quick, according to the laws of this realm.

Review

FULL LEADED

A car review by Julian Fawcett

Whilst no MP likes to be suspended from the Commons, there are some advantages to having a little time off. Getting my golf handicap down, for example, or racking up some lengths in my new swimming pool (to keep me fit for office). But when the Daily Despatch offered me the keys to four of the best cars of 1990, I grabbed them with both driving-gloved hands!

MAZDA MX-5

The four-wheeled equivalent of a page-three stunner! When I took this beauty for a spin down Chipping Norton High Street, heads turned faster than the crowd at a Borg v McEnroe Wimbledon final. When you put your foot down you'll be at 'love all' in no time!

I took her for a spin down to my favourite wine shop in Chipping Camden and when I hit the open road she popped my cork right away. You could feel the petrol burning in the magnificent 1.6 engine, there's nothing like the sound of CO2 being pumped into the atmosphere in high volume! I haven't felt anything hit me that hard since Maggie's handbag after my by-election defeat in '82. When I stopped at some traffic lights, it pulled away quicker than a prudish secretary at the office Christmas party!

JULIAN'S VERDICT:
Sex on wheels. Go for a drive on your own, but don't expect that passenger seat to stay empty!

THE SCORES:
Wow Factor: 10
Golf Club Boot space: 7 – *OK, but had to put my driver in the passenger seat. (First time for everything!)*
Neighbours' Jealousy Factor: 9 – *They'll go greener than a CND protester.*
Family Factor: 10 – *There's no room for the kids in the back so, RESULT! (I'm joking of course.)*

KEWET 1 ELECTRIC CITICAR

When I was given the keys to this tiny electric car from Denmark I thought it was for my one-year-old daughter. It looks like one of those pedal cars that I push her around in when I play with her all the time at home. When I drove it I wished it did have pedals. The company aims to take the UK by storm with its "pop to the shops" eco ethos, but honestly, I could get to the shops quicker if I crawled there on my hands and knees! I like to hear stuff burning when I drive, not the whir of an electric tin opener. And as for looks, it makes Del

Boy's Reliant Robin look like a Lamborghini Countach.

JULIAN'S VERDICT:
Stick to making Lego guys! These electric shoe boxes are never going to take off, ozone layer or no ozone layer.

THE SCORES:
Wow Factor: 0 – *Unless it's: "Wow what a heap of junk."*
Golf Club Boot Space 0 – *You're having a laugh aren't you? There's barely enough room for your spikes.*
Neighbours' Jealousy Factor: 0 – *Unless they're the unfortunate owner of a Sinclair C5!*
Family Factor: 0 – *Forget kids, you'll be lucky if you still have a wife after she sees you driving around in this ladies' handbag.*

BMW 5 SERIES TOURING

This is the perfect car for any good Conservative. Reliable, safe, cost efficient, it's Norman Lamont with an exhaust! This is the sort of car that will get nods of approval from both sides of the house.

There's nothing not to like. It's so good I bought one myself (for driving to Parliament and back). And when I pull it into the Commons underground car park, even the cockney valet gives it a respectful smile. There'll be no Guy Fawkes night explosives put under Parliament while the 5 Series is parked there!

JULIAN'S VERDICT:
Safest car on the road, even after a drink or two.

THE SCORES:
Wow Factor: 5 – *Less wow, more bow (in respect).*
Golf Club Boot Space: 10 – *Enough for you, your mate and his secretary!*
Neighbours' Jealousy Factor: 6 – *Though of course this depends who your neighbours are.*
Family Factor: 10 – *It's two-point-four children heaven. Like I always say: Family! Family! Family!*

RED LOTUS ESPRIT TURBO SE.

The name's Fawcett, Julian Fawcett. No, I'm not James Bond sadly, but I did test drive the latest version of the Lotus Esprit Turbo, as featured in the 1977 film The Spy Who Loved Me, and I can certainly say that this car left me shaken, and more than a little stirred!

This car is the driving equivalent of Labour leader Neïl Kinnock: it's red, noisy and gives me a pain in my backside. In short, it's all mouth and no trousers. (Apologies for putting an image of an MP with no trousers on in your mind, perish the thought!)

Don't even get me started on the seats, I'm still numb from the waist downwards. They're more uncomfortable than a select committee. grilling. I must admit it moves faster than the chief whip before a members' ballot, but in terms of handling it leaves a lot to be desired. The Falklands War was handled better!

JULIAN'S VERDICT:
Treat this car like you would the empty box next to your Labour candidate at the next election – steer clear of it if you want to keep your money!

THE SCORES:
Wow factor: 10 – *But looks aren't everything, thank God, or else I'd be single!*
Golf Club Boot Space: 2 – *Fine if you're Ronnie Corbett, but not if you use adult-sized clubs!*
Neighbours' Jealousy Factor: 10 – *Until they see your garage bills, then 0!*
Family factor: 0 – *You won't have one if you spend too much time sitting on these seats (ouch)!*

POLICE   This interview is being tape recorded. I am ▆Sec 38 1 (a)▆ based at ▆Sec 38 1 (a)▆ which is in the jurisdiction of Berkshire Police. Also present is Mr Butcher, who has declined the offer of legal representation at this time.

PB   No need for formalities mate.

POLICE   Please, address me as Inspector Morris.

PB   Right ho.

POLICE   To confirm, you have agreed to come to the station to help in an ongoing investigation. And you are not under arrest or under any suspicion at this time.

PB   Glad to hear it ma . . . Inspector.

POLICE   Can you confirm your full name please?

PB   Patrick Bobby Butcher.

POLICE   Mr Butcher . . .

PB   Please call me Pat.

POLICE   Pat. You are friends with Tommy Bohnner? Otherwise known as 'Night Owl' . . .

PB   Yep! We talk on the dials. Ehm radio . . .

POLICE   CB radio?

PB   That's right! It stands for Citizens Band radio . . .

    (silence)

PB   . . . Yeah, we'd talk most nights. He's a trucker you see. The CB helps when you're lonely and haven't got any company . . .

POLICE   You're married with a son?

PB   That is correct, yes.

    (silence)

POLICE   Do you remember the last time you spoke with Mr Bohnner?

PB   Been a while . . . About a month ago?

POLICE   What did you talk about, Pat?

PB   Well . . . he hadn't been on his normal frequency for a week. Suddenly he 'came alive' CB talk. Seemed a bit hot and bothered. Turns out he'd got himself into a spot of trouble. He didn't want to say at first. Then he said, "Something bad has happened, what have I done? There's blood everywhere." And, well, I knew exactly what he meant. "Road kill?" I asked, and he says, "Something like that," and that he needed to clear it up. So I told him not to panic and not to worry. It's happened to me. I hit a badger on the 409 out by Yattendon.

1

	I asked him how heavy it was and he said, "About as heavy as a man," so I figured it must have been a deer. I said, "You're probably best cutting it up and shifting it on a tarp." But he said he wasn't sure if he could do it - which is understandable, cos they're big buggers, deers. So I asked what kind of tools he had and he said he only had a 225 hacksaw. I said, "Bloody hell Night Owl! A 225?! That'll take you all night . . ."
POLICE	Go on . . .
PB	So I told him: "What you need is a bloody great circular saw, mate!" And I know he lives round my way so I told him to go to the hardware shop on Portman Road. My pal Ted works there, and he owes me a favour . . .
POLICE	Right . . .
PB	Just tell him Pat sent you and he'll give you a discount. Then I asked if he had any digging tools . . .
POLICE	And did he?
PB	Did he heck! I said while you're there make sure you buy a large groundbreaker spade . . .
	(silence)
PB	He kept saying, "I should report this. I need to make this right." But I told him, "That's only with dogs. All you need to do is clear the path for other road users and to stop the possibility of other animals getting hit while they feed off the carcass . . ."
	(silence)
PB	". . . so you need to chop it up and get it buried mate and make sure you dig four to six feet down. Failing that you could always dissolve it in a drop of lye . . ."
POLICE	Oh my god . . .
PB	Yep. Well it's common sense in't it? (chuckling) He said if I ever tell anyone about this he'll murder me! (chuckling) I did laugh and then he said, "I'm serious, Pat." Honestly these truckers . . . hey? (chuckling) Though it was a little dark for my taste. Yes yes.
	(silence)
PB	So what's this all about?
POLICE	Tommy Bohnner is wanted on suspicion of murdering his next-door neighbour . . .
PB	Ok. Right . . .
	(silence)
PB	Actual murder? Of a human person?
POLICE	Yep . . .
PB	Bloody hell. You think you know someone! Wish I hadn't lent him the car now.

"I have a lot of dreams,
and most of them are
about women."

THOMAS

NAME

THOMAS

WHERE WERE YOU BORN?

In a prison. Not an actual prison, you understand, but a prison of the soul, caged by the stifling rules and suffocating decorum of affluent society. How I cried into my silk pillow as a bairn, yearning for the freedom of a street urchin, idly wandering, bare feet to the cobbles. But, in time, I found my comfort in the bosom of the arts; the sanctuary of words.

HOW DID YOU DIE?

For love. For honour. I was moved to duel an officer of the British Army who, as you know, I believed had insulted my beloved Isabelle Higham whose affections towards me I had that day been deceitfully misled (by my cousin Francis) to believe had evaporated. In that sense, I'm not sure what ultimately killed me, the musket ball or the broken heart — it was the musket ball.

FAVOURITE FOOD?

Ah! so many delicacies swim through my mind. Great breakfasts of eggs, kidneys, chops and liver. Dinners of game, fish and such buttery, buttery vegetables. But nothing to my mind can compare to the exquisite comely sweetness of a peach in season. The soft, velvety skin, almost blushing under your fingers, embarrassed by her beauty. The honeyed scent that whispers to your nose of the secrets within, and finally the fulsome, juicy sweetness that bursts into your mouth, like heaven's own treacle.

FAVOURITE DRINK?

Port and Lemon. Bittersweet as life itself.

FAVOURITE SONG?

Now, here I have to thank you, Alison, for introducing us to such a treasure trove of popular modern recording artists. As you know I have a particular fondness for The Smiths but if I had to pick a single favourite song it would be 'Love Hurts' by Emmylou Harris and Gram Parsons. No person living or dead ever put it better, damn their eyes.

FAVOURITE SPORT?

I did enjoy the volleyball when you put the Olympics on the television. We played it here once with Humphrey's head but he made such a fuss there was never another chance to.

BIGGEST REGRET?

I would have liked to know what it felt like to share a kiss with a person you love. I rather regret challenging that officer to a duel. In retrospect, a more critical attitude toward Francis' comments would have helped.

FONDEST MEMORY?

The day you arrived in the house, Alison.

WORST TRAIT?

I must confess my passions do overwhelm me at times. Like Vesuvius, I may seem at peace, in beautiful repose, but my thoughts and feelings are always bubbling under the surface, white-hot, and I can erupt at any moment with all the heat and fury of God's wrath. It can be trying to live with an artist but you must accept that such outbursts are a price worth paying for their talents, that they spring from the same source as the original thinking and artistic insight that illuminates the world and without which you would be stumbling through your days, deaf, dumb and blind to life's rich bounty.

ANY WORDS OF WISDOM?

So many. I am, of course, a man of words, so …. Yes. So many to choose from. So many words. Words. May I get back to you?

BBC1

6.00 Breakfast **9.15** Morning Live **10.00** Claimed and Shamed **10.45** Fraud Squad **11.15** Homes under the Hammer

12.15 **Bargain Hunt** Two teams compete for the best deal

1.00 **News and Weather**

1.45 **Doctors** The surgery deals with a difficult patient

2.15 **Money for Nothing** Sarah Moore upcycles a sofa and a wicker chair

3.00 **Escape to the Country** A retired couple are looking to relocate to Suffolk

3.45 **Garden Rescue** An urban garden is transformed into a peaceful retreat

4.30 **Clean It, Fix It** Today the team tackles a flat in Bournemouth

5.15 **Pointless** Quiz show hosted by Alexander Armstrong

6.00 News and Weather _Lady B_

7.00 **The One Show** Live chat and topical features, Gyles Brandreth explores The Lost Gardens of Heligan

7.30 **EastEnders** A surprise guest arrives at the Vic

8.00 **Waterloo Road** A fight in the playground isn't quite what it seems

9.00 **The Great British Sewing Bee** 12 Art Week

10.00 **News and Weather**

10.40 **Have I Got More News For You** Political quiz show (R)

11.40 **Glow Up: Britain's Next Make-Up Star** Amazing transformations

12.00 Weather for the Week Ahead **12.25** BBC News

BBC2

6.00 Coast to Coast Food Festival **6.30** Clean It, Fix It **7.15** Garden Rescue **8.00** Hidden Treasures of the National Trust **9.00** Nicky Campbell **11.00** News

12.15 **Politics Live** Conversation about the day's issues

1.00 **The Super League Show** Big names and games from rugby league

1.45 **Impossible** Quiz show hosted by Rick Edwards

2.30 **The Hairy Bikers: Go North** Dave and Si explore the Peak District

3.30 **Home is Where the Art Is** An artwork for a family in Yorkshire

4.15 **Celebrity Antiques Road Trip** The teams are in Sussex.

5.15 **Flog It!** Treasures in the attic

6.00 **Richard Osman's House of Cards** Celebrity quiz

6.30 **Great Railway Journeys** The Glacier Express

7.00 **Women's Test Cricket** Round up of the day

8.00 **Wonders of the Universe with Brian Cox** The moon

9.00 **University Challenge** Lancaster take on Exeter

9.30 **Only Connect** The lateral-thinking quiz _Robin_

10.00 **QI** Comedy panel game

10.30 **Newsnight**

11.00 **Match of the Day 2** Goals, drama and analysis _Pat_

12.00 Countryfile **1.00** Gods of Tennis **2.00** Frontline Fightback **3.00** Big Little Crimes **4.00** Rip Off Britain **5.00** Spy in the Ocean

ITV1

6.00 Good Morning Britain **9.00** Lorraine _Lady B_

10.00 **This Morning** All the best stories, chat, fashion and food

12.30 **Loose Women** Topical daily chat show _Mary_

1.30 **News and Weather**

2.00 **Dickinson's Real Deal** Dealer day at the National Motorcycle Museum, Solihull

3.00 **Tenable** Five new contestants compete to win £125,000

4.00 **Tipping Point** General knowledge quiz hosted by Ben Shephard

5.00 **The Chase** Can the contestants beat the Chasers?

6.00 **Local News and Weather**

6.30 **News and Weather**

7.30 **Emmerdale** A storm is brewing in the village but help comes from an unexpected source

8.00 **Coronation Street** Tempers are heated at the Rovers

9.00 **Long Lost Family: Born without a Trace** A man abandoned as a baby discovers his extraordinary family history, hosted by Davina McCall and Nicky Campbell

10.00 **News and Weather**

10.30 **Local News and Weather** Today's round-up from your area

10.45 **FILM** **Bridget Jones: The Edge of Reason** (2004)

12.00 Teleshopping **3.00** All Elite Wrestling: Dynamite **4.15** Unwind with ITV1 **5.30** James Martin's French Adventure

CHANNEL 4

6.00 Countdown **6.45** Cheers **7.35** The King of Queens **8.25** Frasier **9.55** Find It, Fix It, Flog **10.55** Couples Come Dine with Me **11.55** News

12.00 **Steph's Packed Lunch** Live from Leeds Dock

2.10 **Countdown** Word and number quiz with Colin Murray, Rachel Riley an Susie Dent

3.00 **A Place in the Sun** A retired couple are searching for a lakeside villa in the French Alps

4.00 **Chateau DIY** Buying ar renovating in France

5.00 **Sarah Beeny's New Country Lives** Plucky country-life newbies embrace their fresh sta in the beautiful Cotswo

6.00 **The Simpsons**

6.30 **Hollyoaks** A phone message reveals all

7.00 **News**

8.00 **Gogglebox** Britain's sharpest armchair criti

9.00 **Grand Designs** Londo escapees risk going bankrupt when a serie of disasters hit their ambitious eco house in Somerset

10.00 **Rowing the Atlantic with Ben Fogle and James Cracknell** The pair continue to battle the mental and physic challenges of their ep voyage _Captair_

11.00 **8 out of 10 Cats Doe Countdown** Quiz sh hosted by Jimmy Car

12.00 Taskmaster **1.05** The Lateish Show with Mo Gillig **2.00** Ramsey's Kitchen Nightmares **2.50** Grand Des Australia **3.45** George Clark Amazing Spaces **4.30** The Neighbourhood **5.30** The Neighbourhood

CHANNEL 5

6.00 Milkshake! **9.15** Jeremy Vine **11.15** Storm Huntley

12.00 Alexis Conran News and views on the important stories

1.40 News

1.45 Home and Away There's a new face in Summer Bay

2.15 FILM Ladies in Lavender (2004) Star-studded British period drama set in a picturesque Cornish fishing port

4.00 Paul Martin's Antiques Showdown The popular auctioneer is at Raby Castle in County Durham

5.00 News

6.00 Eggheads Can the challengers beat the Eggheads?

7.00 Michael Ball's Wonderful Wales Michael explores the mountains and valleys of Snowdonia

8.00 The Yorkshire Vet Julian and the veterinary team treat a three-legged cat with a tumour on its knee

9.00 Motorhoming with Merton and Webster Paul and wife Suki go seal-watching off the west coast of Scotland

10.00 Ambulance: Code Red A 43-year-old engineer fights for his life after he is knocked off his bike

11.30 FILM Body Heat (1981) Erotic thriller starring Kathleen Turner and William Hurt

1.30 Teleshopping **3.00** The Yorkshire Vet **3.55** GP: Behind Closed Doors **5.30** Entertainment News

Julian (watch live + record)

ITV2

6.00 Totally Bonkers Guinness World Records **6.35** Love Bites **9.30** Dress to Impress **11.30** Supermarket Sweep **12.35** In for a Penny **1.15** Catchphrase **2.15** **FILM** Dawn of the Planet of the Apes (2014)

5.00 One Tree Hill *Kitty*

6.00 Celebrity Catchphrase

7.00 Alan Carr's Epic Gameshow

8.00 Superstore

8.30 Superstore

9.00 Love Island

10.00 Family Guy **11.00** American Dad **11.30** **FILM** Scream 2 **1.30** CelebAbility **2.15** Totally Bonkers Guinness World Records **3.00** Teleshopping

FOOD NETWORK

7.00 Girl Meets Farm **7.30** Girl Meets Farm **8.00** Simply Raymond Blanc **9.00** Rachel Khoo's Chocolate **9.30** Rachel Khoo's Chocolate **10.00** Bake Off: The Professionals **11.00** Bake Off: The Professionals **12.00** Hairy Bikers: Route 66 **1.00** Hairy Bikers: Route 66 **2.00** Barefoot Contessa **2.30** Barefoot Contessa **3.00** Barefoot Contessa **3:30** Gok Wan's Easy Asian

4.00 Food & Drink *Pat + Julian*

5.00 The Kitchen

6.00 Guy's Grocery Games

7.00 Bake Off: The Professionals

8.00 Michel Roux's Provence Masterclass

9.00 Ottolenghi's Mediterranean Feast

10.00 The Hairy Bikers: Go North

11.00 Restaurant: Impossible **12.00** Ainsley's Good Mood Food **1.00** Teleshopping

DISCOVERY

6.00 Wheeler Dealers
7.00 Deadliest Catch
8.00 Building off the Grid
9.00 Building off the Grid
10.00 How It's Made
10.30 How It's Made 11.00 Undercover Billionaire 12.00 Undercover Billionaire 1.00 Gold Rush: White Water 2.00 Gold Rush: White Water 3.00 Diesel Brothers 4.00 Gold Divers 5.00 Gold Divers

6.00 Hitler's Secret Superweapons *Captain*

7.00 Wheeler Dealers

8.00 Blowing up History

9.00 Naked and Afraid XL

10.00 Street Outlaws

11.00 Moonshiners **12.00** Teleshopping

COMEDY CENTRAL

6.00 Teleshopping **8.00** Guessable? **9.00** The Middle **9.30** The Middle **10.00** The Middle **10.30** The Middle **11.00** Becker **11.30** Becker **12.00** Becker **12.30** Becker **1.00** Becker **1.30** Friends **2.00** Friends **2.30** Friends **3.00** Friends **3.30** Friends **4.00** Cheers **4.30** Cheers *Thomas*

5.00 The Office

5.30 The Office

6.00 The Office

6.30 The Office

7.00 The Office

7.30 The Office

8.00 Michael McIntyre: Live & Laughing

9.00 FILM Scary Movie (2000)

10.45 Reno 911 **11.15** Reno 911 **11.45** Most Ridiculous **12.15** Most Ridiculous **12.45** South Park **1.20** South Park **1.55** South Park **2.30** Teleshopping

PICK OF THE DAY

WONDERS OF THE UNIVERSE WITH BRIAN COX
After last week's deep dive into neighbouring galaxies, Professor Cox is back closer to home tonight, exploring our relationship with the moon. Or, rather, with our closest moon, as some scientists believe we actually have three . . .

HITLER'S SECRET SUPERWEAPONS
Back for a second series (it seems that Hitler had an awful lot of secrets) this episode focuses on the V-3 'Supergun', designed to bombard London with 600 shells per hour, and a bizarre rifle that fired around corners (and turned out to be less-than-super).

ITV1 VARIATIONS

ANGLIA No variations
BORDER No variations
CENTRAL No variations
CHANNEL No variations
GRANADA No variations
LONDON No variations
MERIDIAN No variations
TYNE TEES No variations
WEST No variations
WESTCOUNTRY No variations
YORKSHIRE No variations

EVERYTHING IS FINE

TRUST ME. I'VE GOT THIS.

VOTE CONSERVATIVE ON APRIL 9TH

VOTE CONS ON APR

As you
in governm

LOWER TAXES!
That means more
money in YOUR pock
Why give your mone

MON£Y

It does, will and
can trickle dow

BAN THE UNIONS!
Do you need a nurse to treat that wound? Well, TOUGH, she's on strike! Unions mean that people can go on

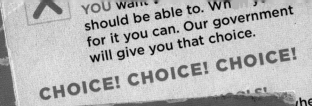

YOU want ... should be able to. Wh... for it you can. Our government will give you that choice.

CHOICE! CHOICE! CHOICE!

...many people worry about ...oney. Of course they do. ...s how the world turns.

...ut we want you to know ...at you don't need to ...o anything except keep ...orking hard.

...ecause the people at the ...op of the tree are busy ...haking the branches so you ...get the acorns you deserve.

...And no one is shaking them harder than your local Conservative candidate **JULIAN FAWCETT.**

...In fact, there's only one thing he wants to shake more than those branches...

...And that's your hand.

VOTE CONSERVATIVE

GENERAL ELECTION 1991

All you have to do is tick this box on 9th April

Polling stations will be open 7am to 10pm

Julian **FAWCETT**

June 6th 1940

Flavers left yesterday. For Africa. Nothing
I could do to dissuade him.
It will all be over by Christmas.

I'm sure of it.

HERTS AND BEDS REGIMENT
BUTTON HOUSE HQ

N.A.A.F.I
HOME FORCES CANTEEN

```
cc   oo   cc   k  k   sss   oo   cc
c  c o  o c  c k k    s    o  o c  c
c    o  o c    kk     ss   o  o c
c  c o  o c  c k k     s   o  o c  c
cc   oo   cc   k  k   sss   oo   cc
```

(Cocktail Society)

At ease!

With morale ever at the forefront of my mind, and after a fruitful chinwag with the boys in procurement, I'm delighted to announce that you can once again imbibe of my famous Cock Soc.

Cocktails will be served from 1600 hours on Fridays, and may be drunk on the lawn, weather permitting, providing any divots are heeled back in.

Cpl Norriss will be back on flutes and gimlets, or if you prefer something long or stiff, Lt Minards is your man.

All the classic martinis and sours are available, though I would strongly recommend one of our 'Button House' specials, devised by Minards (with modest input from yours truly).

So go on, let your hair down*

NAAFI Drinks Menu
June 1944

THE DAMBUSTER - Two fingers of gin, a nip of bitters, rosemary garnish (optional), prune juice. Drink only when close to facilities.

BREN DRILLS - Half a stout, finger of gin, syrup, twist of lemon to garnish. Prepare ingredients. Mix yourself as fast as you can. Your partner may then inspect the cocktail.

TALL BOY - Tall glass of Champagne, syrup, cherry (if available). Mix. When ready to drink, the command should be given: "Bombs ready!" Drop in one finger of gin. Shout, "Bombs gone!" Then drink.

THE EAGLE'S NEST - A finger of schnapps, Pilsner beer, egg, edelweiss or similar delicate flower to garnish. Mix gently. Drink at leisure.

BATTLE OF BRITAIN - Half a pint of bitter, half a pint of Pilsner. Drink at attention.

BLITZKRIEG - Two measures schnapps, one measure gin, one measure whisky, one measure beer, one measure wine, a sprinkle of pepper. Tends to be last of the evening.

* (Hair should remain regulation length; one drink maximum; off-duty personnel only.)

At the table

f you are fortunate enough to be asked to dinner, unimpeachable conduct and impeccable table manners must be maintained for every second of the evening. One slovenly mistake and you risk permanent ostracism from polite society. If you accept such an invitation before you have memorised this chapter in its entirety, you do so at your own incalculable risk!

Never ask for food. When it is offered to you it is good manners to accept it, but it is a sign of ill-breeding to ask for a dish to be passed to you. If a dish proves to be unpalatable to your tastes, the best course of action is to fix your face into a smile so as to give the impression you are enjoying it. Perhaps try to remember a dish you do enjoy and focus on the memory of that rather than the abomination in your mouth. If that does not work, focus on the simple mechanical act of chewing ten times and then swallowing. With a particularly repugnant mouthful, it can help if one can discreetly take a sip of water to flush it away with.

Never make a noise while eating. Nothing is more gruesome than the sound of mastication and lip-smacking. Some people think it tolerable to express pleasure in their food by making humming and cooing noises as they dine; personally I find it beastly and revolting. Such noises belong in a brothel, not at a dinner table.

Always cut your food into small pieces, the smaller the better. It is vulgar for a lady to open her mouth and thus, when doing so, it is imperative to keep the aperture as small as humanly possible. I once dined with a countess who more than once raised a fork to her mouth with no apparent food on it at all. Such exquisite manners.

Never speak while eating. There is nothing more abominable, and no surer sign of ill-breeding, than the sight of a person attempting to form words around a mouthful of vol-au-vent. However, it is impolite to stay mute at the table, it gives the impression that you are. a gluttonous person, too consumed with the act of filling your stomach to participate in polite conversation. Be sure to converse with those close to you, at a decorous level. Refrain from raising your voice to anyone seated further away. Never make an inquiry or ask a question of a companion who has a mouthful themselves. If you realise you are speaking to someone in this position, find a way to expand your question so that it reaches its natural conclusion when they have swallowed their tongue. Not *their* tongue, I mean the tongue they are eating (jellied ox tongue in this example).

Never neglect to eat. Just as it is rude to eat and not speak, it is equally a sign of low background to speak and not eat. It will be taken either as a harsh judgement of the hosts' food or as a sign that you have already dined before the engagement. Monstrous, in either case. The art of dinner-conversation is one of timing. You must choose carefully when to eat and when to speak.

At the table, you must *never gesticulate* under any circumstances. You risk a calamitous collision with the contents of the table in front of you. Glasses can be smashed, liquids can be spilled, candles may be knocked over, setting the entire dining room aflame, all for the sake of your lack of expressive restraint. If you *must* animate your point, do so with your facial features.

Refrain from all bodily functions. If you must sneeze or cough, excuse yourself from the table as promptly as possible, pausing to bow to the host and the gathered company, and retire to the next room to do so. If you absolutely cannot take the time to excuse yourself, at least have the decency to dive off your chair and under the table. When you return to your seat, acknowledge your vulgarity, look at the floor and remain silent for the rest of the meal so that everybody knows you are thoroughly ashamed of yourself.

My Grand Tour: A Journal
by Thomas Thorne

I have, of late, been suffering a most
tortuous blockage. What once flowed freely,
positively gushing out of me, somehow has
ceased and now, for all my efforts, however
hard I strain, nothing is produced.

I speak of inspiration, of words, of verse.
Some mysterious impediment holds them back,
and it seems the more days and weeks go by
without release, the more agonising the
impediment, as though it is building up
in me, waiting to come out. I fear that when
it finally bursts out, it will be a most
exhausting and painful exertion. But let me
have it, I say! Let me submit myself to
the muse!

To that end I have arranged a voyage,
a great European excursion. What better
way to stir up the senses? To arouse the
passions? To excite the imagination? If
anything can inspire a poet to dig deep into
his mother tongue for phrases that do justice
to the majesty of his subjects, to stretch

himself to the very skies to find new heights of expression, to harness the written word to the task of vivid evocation like a wild horse to the task of pulling a plough or whatever farmers do with horses... If anything can move a poet to pick up his pen and write, then surely it is the great gothic spire of Notre-Dame, the tulip fields of the Netherlands, the domes of the Berlin Cathedral and the magnificent ruins of the great Roman Empire in Italy.

We set sail tomorrow to adventure. To inspiration!

Paris

I am quite tired from the journey, the crossing of the water in particular, which made me very sick. Much of the countryside is remarkably similar to our own fair England and quite lovely. The roads are rather shoddy, however, and the rolling of the carriage did little to remedy the lingering effects of the seasickness. Enough of the tedious journey though, for today I finally saw with my own eyes, the Notre-Dame de Paris, the symbol of the city of Paris! It was ever so big and the feeling of being there was very nice indeed. ~~It was very~~ I think I shall let it settle in my mind and return to further description later. I definitely will do that, I am just a little tired and, come to think of it, I have been speaking mostly French these last few days so perhaps that is why the English vocabulary is a little harder to recall.

Amsterdam

Blue skies and a fresh breeze to see the tulip fields which were vast and colourful and really very nice and on the whole it was most pleasant to see them.

Rome

Beautiful sunshine. The Colosseum, The Pantheon, the Trevi Fountain,

St. Peter's Basilica, the Sistine Chapel, all so nice in their own different ways.

Athens

Acropolis nice. Weather too hot and not nice.

Vienna
Nice.

Munich.
Very nice

Flanders. Also nice.

Home at last and ready to reflect on my many and varied experiences abroad and finally turn them to use; to pick up my pen and write something astoundingly, astonishingly, undeniably nice.

I think I shall start tomorrow.

LEVEL 0
ALIVE

You're completely alive and can do anything — some embroidery, have a swim, eat a pineapple, anything. Everyone gets to do this layer, but only very special people get to come back in the next layer.

LEVEL 1
GHOST

You're dead but your spirit remains where you died. Living people can't see or hear you (apart from you, Alison), but you can see and hear them.

LEVEL 3
THE REALM OF UNICORNS

To reach this level, you must pass through the Gate of Herbert. I'm not sure exactly where this is or what it looks like, but, luckily, you get led to it by a kindly wizard with a long grey beard and a dragon tattoo — The Wizard Larsson.

You can still see and hear all the ghosts and the ghost-ghosts, but now you can also play with the unicorns! I think Herbert looks after the unicorns, like a shepherd. A unicherd. Unicorns eat rainbows, which are grown in magic faraway pots by Titchmarsh, the constant gardener. He then sells them to Herbert but Pat wasn't sure what currency they use.

LEVEL 4
THE 39 STEPS OF LUDLUM

This level is reached by some sort of staircase. Again, don't worry about finding it, as the Great Gatsby (also a wizard I think) will show you the way in return for some food — the grapes of wrath. You can still see the unicorns from here, but they can't see you.

Anyway, this layer is home to Ludlum. Pat was quite vague about what Ludlum looks like and what he actually does, but (after much questioning) it turns out this is because he's an imposter! The REAL Ludlum was kidnapped by the evil Lionel Witchenwardrobe. I wondered if Lionel may have taken Ludlum into the next layer and Pat said that's exactly what had happened and that we must make haste!

LEVEL 2
GHOST-GHOST

You remain where you were a ghost, but now the ghosts can't see or hear you either. (Except maybe if you were to die and become a ghost, Alison? You might be able to see ghost-ghosts! Oh, I can't wait to find out. I hope you die soon. Gosh, I don't mean that.)

You only remain on this level for three months.

After Mary left us, Kitty was very upset. So Pat tried to make her feel better and ... well this is now what Kitty thinks happens when Ghosts move on.

LEVEL 5
LORD OF THE RING-FLIES

Apparently you reach this level through a completely normal door (I think we are still inside the house in some way, so that makes sense).

You can still see Gatsby from this layer, but now he can't see you. Anyway, it turns out that Lionel had delivered Ludlum to the evil King Stephen, Lord of the Ring-Flies! But he gets all his power from the orb of Holcroft, which I suggested we steal to free Ludlum, and Pat said that was a very good idea.

LEVEL 6
THE CASTLE OF TOLSTOY

You must cross a bridge to reach the safety of the Castle of Tolstoy. You can still see King Stephen from here, but he can't see you, which is a relief. It's a really lovely castle and you can be very happy here, which is nice because this is the last level where everyone finds peace.

So, that's how it all works.

Do let me know if you have any questions.

Portrait (damaged) of Sir Humphrey Bone (1531–1575). Artist unknown. Localised fire damage to canvas sustained 2022.

Portrait (damaged) of Sir Humphrey Bone (1531-1575).
Artist unknown. Sizeable tear to canvas.

"A lady does not hold
a carrot like that!"

LADY BUTTON

NAME

LADY BUTTON

WHERE WERE YOU BORN?

Chichester General Infirmary. I believe it was a Tuesday, and, as my father would often say, 'Tuesday's Child is Full of Grace,' which, of course, I am. Next question.

HOW DID YOU DIE?

Must I really delve into this again, Alison? Ugh. I found George deep in, what Julian has since told me is termed, a 'Moroccan Tea Party' betwixt Henry, our gardener, and Evans, our butler. When George realised I had seen this spectacle, he decided to launch me from the bedroom window to keep my silence. But I shall not be silenced! Now, I refuse to talk about it any more.

FAVOURITE FOOD?

Soused hog's face.

FAVOURITE DRINK?

A nice sherry cobbler.

FAVOURITE SONG?

'The Old Rugged Cross'. 'While the Convent Bells were Ringing' is also not without its charms, but becomes a little light on convent-related lyrics in latter verses, which bends it too far towards frivolity for my tastes.

FAVOURITE SPORT?

No. Not for me.

BIGGEST REGRET?

I suppose never knowing True Love. Or that time I miscalculated a bridge score.

FONDEST MEMORY?

The day that I met Dante. As soon as I set eyes on him, I knew we would be companions for life. Well, for his life anyway. I outlived him. Though not by as much as I'd been expecting.

WORST TRAIT?

I'm often told I'm bossy. 'Bossy Boots' they've taken to calling me... but I shan't apologise for having standards, Alison... Honestly!

ANY WORDS OF WISDOM?

Yes. Don't get any more tattoos. They make you look cheap.

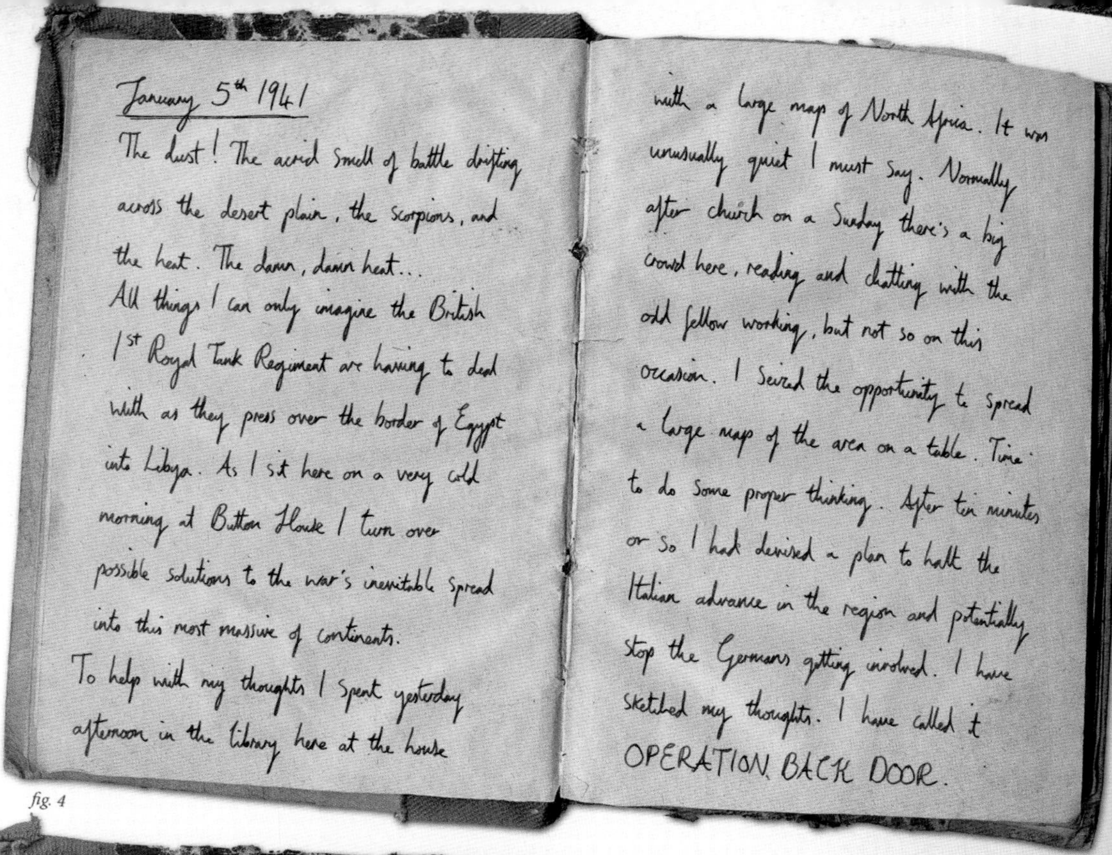

January 5th 1941

The dust! The acrid smell of battle drifting across the desert plain, the scorpions, and the heat. The damn, damn heat...

All things I can only imagine the British 1st Royal Tank Regiment are having to deal with as they press over the border of Egypt into Libya. As I sit here on a very cold morning at Button House I turn over possible solutions to the war's inevitable spread into this most massive of continents.

To help with my thoughts I spent yesterday afternoon in the library here at the house with a large map of North Africa. It was unusually quiet I must say. Normally after church on a Sunday there's a big crowd here, reading and chatting with the odd fellow working, but not so on this occasion. I seized the opportunity to spread a large map of the area on a table. Time to do some proper thinking. After ten minutes or so I had devised a plan to halt the Italian advance in the region and potentially stop the Germans getting involved. I have sketched my thoughts. I have called it OPERATION BACK DOOR.

fig. 4

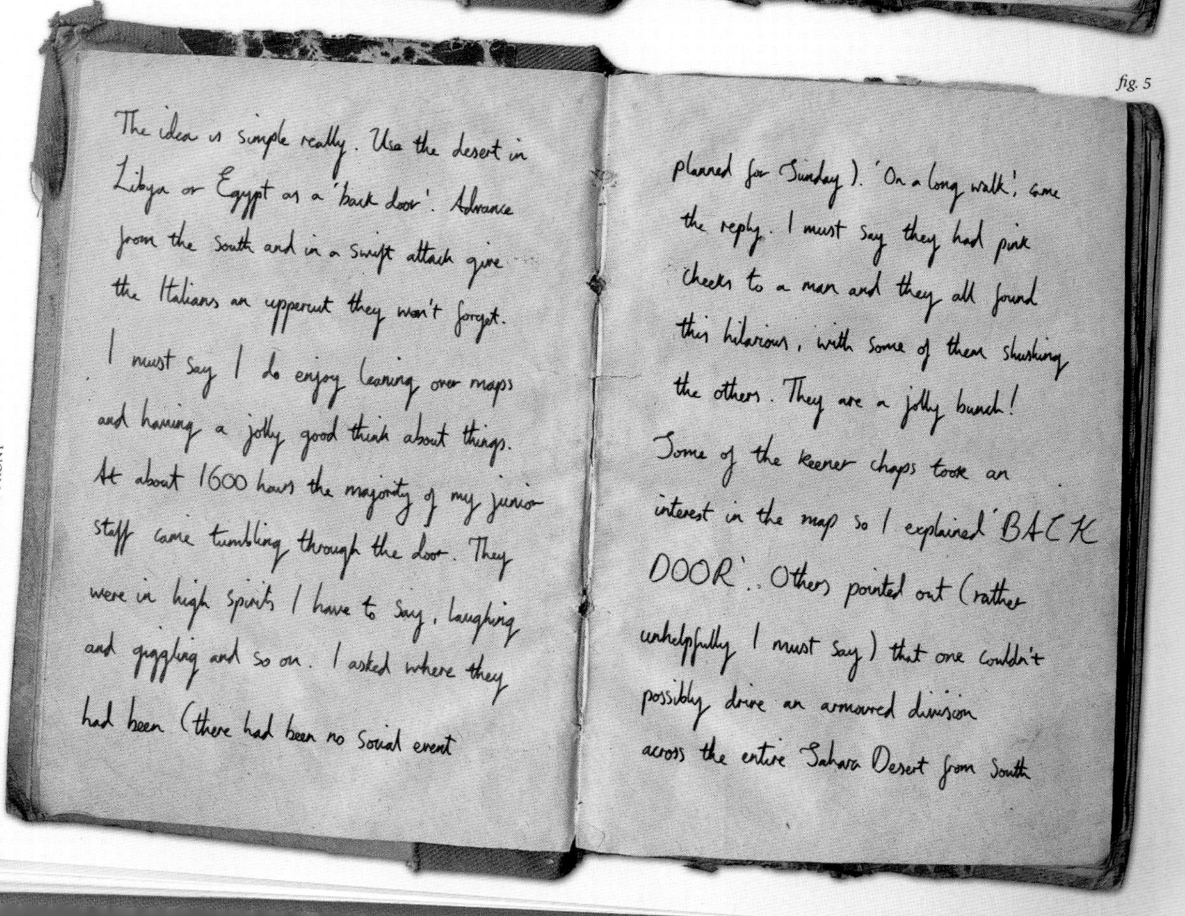

fig. 5

The idea is simple really. Use the desert in Libya or Egypt as a 'back door'. Advance from the south and in a swift attack give the Italians an uppercut they won't forget.

I must say I do enjoy leaning over maps and having a jolly good think about things. At about 1600 hours the majority of my junior staff came tumbling through the door. They were in high spirits I have to say, laughing and giggling and so on. I asked where they had been (there had been no social event planned for Sunday). 'On a long walk', came the reply. I must say they had pink cheeks to a man and they all found this hilarious, with some of them shushing the others. They are a jolly bunch!

Some of the keener chaps took an interest in the map so I explained 'BACK DOOR'. Others pointed out (rather unhelpfully I must say) that one couldn't possibly drive an armoured division across the entire Sahara Desert from south to north. But I say toffee to that! Fortune favours the brave and so on.

Despite the naysayers and doubters, I'm still convinced Op BACK DOOR is a winner. I may well send this plan to Southern Command.

A sense of optimism and cheeriness this evening. I'm sure this whole thing will be over by Christmas!

fig. 6

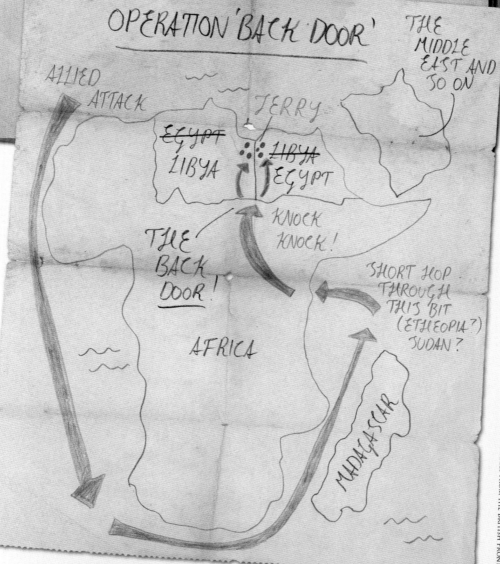

OPERATION 'BACK DOOR'

THE MIDDLE EAST AND SO ON

ALLIED ATTACK

JERRY

EGYPT / LIBYA

LIBYA EGYPT

KNOCK KNOCK!

THE BACK DOOR!

SHORT HOP THROUGH THIS 'BIT (ETHIOPIA?) SUDAN?

AFRICA

MADAGASCAR

ROBIN'S ORAL HISTORY

Occured to me that Robin has seen, like, thousands of years of history and I should probably ask him about that.

Was big walk. Bit cold.
Then bit less cold.
Then hunt. Then bear.
Then dead. Then nothing.
Then new tribe. Then tribe die.
Then nothing. Then more nothing.
Think went mad for a bit. More nothing.
Then man chop tree, make field, then crop.
Then crop die. Then pig. Then pig die. Then man die.
Then nothing. More nothing. Went mad again.
Nothing.
Oh! Saw first pot. Don't really see fuss, but OK pot.
More farm. Stone house. Ugly. New farmer. Ugly.
Saw first bit metal. Member thinking 'look good
for hitting'. But they make plough. Idiot.
Then come big bully with load of other bully.
Say 'farm ours now, you ours now'. Cruel, hard, mean.
Member thinking 'like this guy'. They hang round for
a bit. Then, dunno, bored I guess – off they go.
But all stay same.
Boring. Boring. Went mad again. Pat says is dark
age, but light seem same to me. Dunno.
Then come new guy. Say 'farm ours now, you
ours now' but in different voice to last guy.
Think we got king, but I not meet the guy.
Can't vouch for. Think one called 'Ctun' or
something, which Julian says almost funny.
Then just lot of loud men. But then always
quite a lot loud men.
Then bit of war. Someone win, don't know who.
Someone lose, don't know who. New guy, new voice,

build thing, then son build better thing.
All King now have be called Henry. It law.
More people come. Village now. But all get
cough and scab and then no village any more.
Then bit more war. Both sides look same to me
but I guess one win. Think he won rose or
something. Must have really wanted rose.
New loud man build big house. Then burn down.
So build bigger house.
Saw first book. Don't really see fuss. Only saw
outside, but that seem good way to judge book.
Then think king have problem with 'paypal' so start
own church. But he last Henry as law change and all
King must be called Stewart. Better name. Make sense.
Then new war. Real man fight posh man. Real man win
so kill posh man, but posh man come back anyway.
Then there more coughs and scabs but this one can
be killed by fire, so bit easier to deal with.
The new law say all Stewart must be called George.
Until we get lady king who say she not want to be
called George and she want to be called 'Lady
King Queen Victorian'.
She make special engine that put steam in sky to
make sure sky warm enough. If you make enough steam
it turn to electricity which like tiny bit of thunder
you use to light house which turn out to be LOT of fun.
Then there war but I did not see it.
Then there new war, which take over house, but
house win and war have to leave.
Then war turn cold and telly come along then
you come to house and I get mouse family and
that everything up to just now.
Don't think I miss anything?
No... No, that's it.

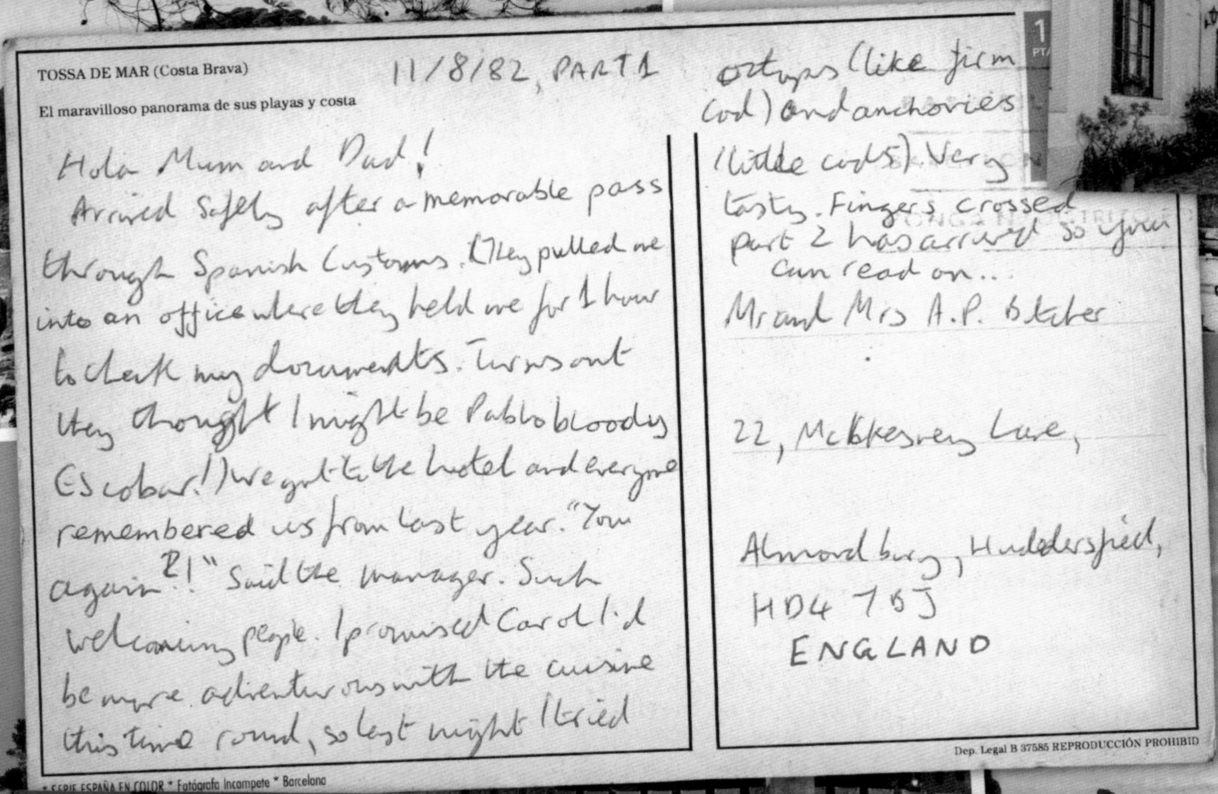

TOSSA DE MAR (Costa Brava)

El maravilloso panorama de sus playas y costa

11/8/82, PART 1

Hola Mum and Dad!
Arrived safely after a memorable pass through Spanish Customs. They pulled me into an office where they held me for 1 hour to check my documents. Turns out they thought I might be Pablo bloody Escobar! We got to the hotel and everyone remembered us from last year. "You again?!" said the manager. Such welcoming people. I promised Carol I'd be more adventurous with the cuisine this time round, so last night I tried

octups (like firm cod) and anchovies (little cods). Very tasty. Fingers crossed part 2 has arrived so you can read on...

Mr and Mrs A.P. Blater

22, McKkesvery Lane,

Almondbury, Huddersfield,
HD4 7SJ
ENGLAND

Dep. Legal B 37585 REPRODUCCIÓN PROHIBID

* SERIE ESPAÑA EN COLOR * Fotógrafa incompleta * Barcelona

Tossa De Mar

T⊙ssa De Mar

1930 – CASTILLO DE TOSSA DE MAR

PART 2

Hola! Daley has made friends with this lad so we've made friends with the parents. Lovely couple. The Dad plays rugby league for Castleford! And by heck he can drink! I tried to keep up with him, blacked out and woke up in the bath with 4 rotisserie chickens! I won't be doing that again but at least we had a lovely lunch on the beach. There was so much leftover chicken we fed a whole chowder of stray cats. Hope you're feeling

better Dad.
See you soon
Love
Patrick, Carol and Daley xx

Mr and Mrs A.P. Butcher

22, McChesney Lane,

Almondbury, Huddersfield

HD4 7BJ

ENGLAND

Foto: R.R Ediciones Luz Solar Barcelona Telf 765 54 345
Prohibida su Reproducción

Deposito Legal B 071071

Tossa de Mar

121

**HERTS AND BEDS REGIMENT
BUTTON HOUSE HQ**

++++++ S E C R E T ++++++

DATE: 5th January 1940   HQ 3 Coy Int. Button House
Issue N°3/7   HEMEL HEMPSTEAD/(857432)

MUNITIONS REQUEST

++++ U R G E N T ++++

ATTENTION:
Lieutenant General Sir Bertie Drew FISHER, K.C.B., C.M.G., D.S.O.
HQ Southern Command

FROM:
Officer Commanding HQ 3 Coy (Int.)

Sir,

I should like to wish you and your staff what I hope will be a very happy, and
indeed victorious, New Year. I'm confident we can whip the army into shape
and organise ourselves into an effective fighting force; show the Germans
what we're made of (tough stuff) and give Hitler a bally good bunch of fives.

With that in mind I submit to you, sir, a request for munitions at HQ 3 Coy (Int.)
Button House.

We have been stationed here for six months. The staff here are eager to fight, and
though our work is very much considered 'back room' by some, we do take on certain
classified operations and we feel that we may present a highly prized target
should Jerry invade, which, as we all know, could be at any moment.

At the time of writing, we are woefully underprepared. We have one full-time guard,
Cpl Bottlesby, who uses the shotgun requisitioned from the House. It has three shells
(one damp which may not fire). He also carries a cricket bat with him as backup.

With this in mind I should like to request the following:

  • Webley Mk IV Service Revolver (10)
  • 3.7 Inch HAA Gun Battery (Anti-Aircraft) and Team.
  • Lee Enfield MkII (30) to be issued to ground team and guards.
  • Bren Mk I Light Machine Gun (4).
  • Grenades/Mines (Various).
  • Very Pistols (Flares) in case they come at night, which, knowing Jerry,
    he will.

I look forward to your reply at your earliest convenience.

Capta

HQ SOUTHERN COMMAND

++++++SECRET++++++

The Office of
Lieutenant General Sir Bertie Drew FISHER, K.C.B., C.M.G., D.S.O.
HQ Southern Command

Captain Oliver Chetterton-Pillar ADC

MUNITIONS REQUEST

++++URGENT++++

ATTENTION:
Officer Commanding
HQ 3 Coy (Int.) Button House/HEMEL HEMPSTEAD/(857432)
DATE: 27th February 1940
Issue N°1

FROM:
Captain Oliver CHETTERTON-PILLAR - ADC to Lt. Gen. FISHER (Southern Command).

Sir,

Thank you for your request for munitions.

You must understand that at this time the General is extremely preoccupied with
organising the key defensive strategy for the country in its hour of need. I hope you
don't take offence that I am replying on his behalf.

Shortages of munitions are a countrywide problem and the General wishes to pass on his
regret that none of your requested list will be granted in the foreseeable future.

We must steel ourselves, sir, for a long campaign. Had the General the time, I know he
would suggest that you should keep your requisitioned weapon oiled, your whistle clean
and your chin up.

     God Save the King!

     Signed:

Capt. Oliver Chetterton-Pillar, Coldstream Guards

Dear Miss Ash,

Well, I truly am perplexed. What a mystery. Do you have a sister, perhaps? I was sure the lady I spoke to was the niece of Joseph Barnham and I was fairly certain the old man who made our introduction called her Jane. I cannot think of another woman's name for which I could have mistaken it. He was a most doddery old fellow so the fault could have been his. A corpulent chap, perhaps the old glut was distracted by the sweet treats upon the table. And the redness of his cheeks belied a fondness for wine, I wouldn't be surprised if he drank himself to sleep soon after, so it is possible he could not make out your face for the fuzziness of his drunken vision. Or perhaps he simply could not see past the great wart on his nose!

Do let me know if you have a sister or if you know of any other ladies it could possibly have been.

Yours curiously

Thomas Thorne

Dear Mr Thorne,

I do not have a sister. The man you so rudely describe is my father though he is not the fat, boozy beast you paint him as, and the mole on his nose is hardly as unsightly as you pretend. I can assure you if he were aware of your description, let alone the wanton, lascivious overtures you have made to me in these letters, you would not survive the week!

Miss Ash

Dear Miss Ash,

I thank you for your reply. I am quite sure it was not your father I was describing so he need not concern himself and, as for my previous correspondence, I feel you may have rather mistaken the meaning of my letters which were meant in a spirit of friendship more than romance. I must be brief as I am very busy with my work.

Yours,

Thomas Thorne

Awards & Badges

Challenge Badges

Orienteering

Natural Disasters

Unnatural Disasters

Responsibility Awards

FIRST AID

FIRE MARSHAL

NEGOTIATOR

Interest Badges

Archery

Camping

Abseiling

Astronomy

Sewing

Wound Care

Helping Hands

Farming

Asthma

Entertainer

Observation

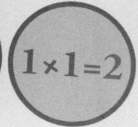
Numeracy

wards

ronze Award: Three Interest Badges
lver Award: Six Interest Badges
old Award: Nine Interest Badges

"This is my house now. I'm not going anywhere."

ALISON

I tells you as was taught to me, but not all hands are blessed of weaving fingers. So be not down at mouth if thy basket does end up a twisted knot of splintered muck.

Afore the weavings is to be done, ye must harvest the wicker. Beware, not all willow be given to the task. If it be frail and does snap whence bent back, like Godric's arm in the forge door, it be not fit for the workings and should be cast aside, like Godric after what happened.

Some willows have bark of differents colours which will make your basket the more special. For a thousand hues are to be found in nature for those of keen eye – brown, light brown, grey-brown, dark brown… the list does go on. Harvesting in winter time be best, or you shall have much work with the strippings of the leaves! Ha ha ha!

1   For this basket, which be five potatoes high, we shall need a fair bundle of wicker worms. In a bunch they should haves the girth of a ripe pumpkin and each worm should be as long as a boy lying down.

2   The worms must be dried out in the sunshine and then wets again by soakings in a pond or stream or like for four moons and suns.

3   Take severals of the thickest worms and cut them the length of a boot or shoe.

4   Thence use your knife to split half of them at the middles. Like they be given of a mouth! (They will not talk though, as they still be sticks.)

5   Take the ones ye did not split and shove them through the ones ye did, as though feeding the mouths! Halt at half fed to form a cross shape at the middle, for this be the slath.

6   Take your two thinnest worms next for weavers, and insert their heads into the split of the slath, at a corner of the mouth. Then turn it and part the weaverworms so the next arm of the slath is between them.

7   Bring the weaver from the back ups and overs the next arm, and its partner overs and unders. Repeat the process til ye be done, turning the slath again and again. You must always pulls the weaver much tightly, lest your basket be full of gaps and you should lose grain through them at harvest, which does make your husband utter of the Lord's name.

8   Next two more weaverworms, but this times weave them between each slath stick, nots the whole arm. Keep weaving around and around and around with a new worm each time the last is nearly at its end. The sticks shall spread wide like the grasping fingers of the bishop in the season of tithes.

9   Once the base be four potatoes wide, it be done.

10 The slath sticks will stick out like legs of a spider. We must take two worms for each leg, sharpen their ends and shove them into the weave as fars as we can both side of each leg. Now our spider has very long legs! Mind it crawls not away! Hahahaha.

11 Now we bend up these legs. Worry not, tis actually a basket, not a spider, and feels not pain.

12 We tethers them to keeps them from droop, with a goodly loop of twine or wool or vine. Or wicker if you has some, which you does.

13 The sticking-out longs of slath at the base can now be lopped off, as John did do to Oswyn's bull.

14 Now we lay the basket pon our lap like a wicker babe. Take three worms and cut them to the same longs.

15 Shove them into the weave of the base as far as a lady's finger, each one to the same side of each spider legs.

16 The first worm dances around two spider legs, then behind the next and out. The next worm does the same dance around the legs. The dance whirls til the worm be at ends, then a new worm is shoved in alongside the old and the dance starts anew.

17 When tis good and thick, press it downs hard and chop away the sticking out ends. Now the bottom be done and the sides can begin!

18 Now the worms do a most simple dance, in and out of each spider leg, round and round and round and round. When a worm is at ends, a new worm cross over and takes up the dance.

19 To finish the basket, the spider legs must be woven in… Bend one leg over with a gap of your thumb or fattest finger above the border. Let it pass two legs and dance behind the third.

20 Let each leg do the same dance til ye be done. Then chop the sticking-outs.

You have made a basket, five potatoes high! This you can use to carry vegetables, bread or a bit of a tree or eggs if you has them. Well done!

mary swears this makes an excellent basket, so I've typed up every detail and I'm going to give it a bash.

Mary, Kitty and Humphrey enjoy a little pre-bedtime reading.

Another fiercely fought game of charades. (Julian's '9½ Weeks' made Fanny leave the room.)

The Captain gives his lecture on amphibious landing craft. Julian sleeps.

Humphrey's head waits to be discovered (day three).

WHO'S THIS TONY BLAIR UPSTART?
HE LOOKS ABOUT 10!

SHADOW SEC FOR EMPLOYMENT

EMPLOYMENT FOR WHAT? NURSERY SCHOOLS?

GORDON BROWN
TEXTURE LIKE SUN!
 what?
The Strangers you bake!
STRANGLERS!!
(Golden Brown!.)
yes, keep up!!   HA HA!!

FAMILY!
FAMILY!
FAMILY!
When did you last
see your FAMILY!!

NORMAN LAMONT'S
HIGH BROWS
how did
he get this
job?

no eyedea!

DOUGLAS
TURD

QUESTION TIME
Doorbells?
or KNOCKERS?
Ha ha!!

Julian Fawcett

HOUSE O
COMMO

Found out that Lady B can be captured on camera so searched every local history book we could find and sure enough...

Wed 1st Jan, 1941

Dear Personnel,

May I begin by wishing each and everyone of you a Happy New Year! And as we rightfully acknowledge our superiority against the enemy in the air, we must not forget the crucial role we all play here at Button House HQ. The intelligence we accumulate is the eyes, ears and ultimately feet, legs, hands, mouth and brain of the British forces and so, as we look ahead to the challenges 1941 will undoubtedly bring, we must stand steadfast, shoulder to shoulder and resolute in our vital duty.

CHRISTMAS CELEBRATIONS / GANG SHOW

After an arduous year of war, I think it did us all the world of good to let off some steam for a short time over the festive period and what better way to celebrate than the gang show!

For those of you who took 48 hours leave, here's a rundown of events -

Our deserved guests of honour this year were the fine men (and women) from RAF Dunham Marsh and Gp Capt. Aitchison insisted on giving a speech where he managed, impeccably, to reiterate everything that I had already said.

The show then commenced with a big opening number, A Can-Can! Performed by four of the burliest Parisian fillies this side of the English Channel - Pte Pink, Pte Dennis, Sgt Scates and Lt Savage gave us a somewhat unwieldy rendition of the famous routine. Pte Dennis, as usual, showing us all a little more cheek than necessary. Excellent energy all round.

Next up was Cpl Bellamy giving us her tremendously powerful and almost perfect performance of We'll Meet Again. Truly earth shattering. I think we're all grateful the windows were sufficiently scrimmed.

Then came 2nd Lt Wilberforce's plate-spinning act, where he attempted to balance six plates on six canes and tried to maintain the gyroscopic motion of each plate until all plates were revolving at the same time! Quite the endeavour. He managed two. Two and a half for a good three seconds or so. In the end the stage resembled a Greek wedding, but it really was a bally, bally good effort.

Finally, the finale of the show. With a stand-out reputation we were fortunate enough to commandeer the skills of a magician, the finest in the division! Or so we were told.

Staff Sgt Page began well with a couple of card tricks that were almost very impressive. He asked Pte Godrush to pick a card and not to say what card it was. Page then took a beef-paste sandwich from Godrush's plate, and there it was! Tucked away inside was the 7 of Diamonds. Godrush's card was actually the 9 of Hearts but they are the same colour so it was very close indeed.

Then, in front of our very eyes he swapped a rabbit for a dove. The trick was splendid but the dove is now loose. I repeat, the dove is loose. I ask you all to please remain vigilant. It's been heard in the rafters at night and has made a terrible mess of the gymnasium. We must find it and kill it.

He then asked for a volunteer and brave Lt Peters stepped up. Didn't surprise me in the slightest. Peters is one of the bravest men I know and has just returned from a stint at the front.

Staff Sgt Page made Peters exhibit his right index finger to the audience, asked him to wiggle it to demonstrate that it was a genuine finger, then placed it into a cigar guillotine and chopped it off. Actually chopped it off. It was meant to be a sleight of hand (no pun intended) but he botched it.

Poor Peters. He had led the retreat to Dunkirk, was strafed by the Luftwaffe on the beach unscathed, only to have Staff Sgt Page chop off his finger. Now he'll never bowl off spin again.

Lt Peters was sent to the infirmary and Page was promptly arrested.

After the commotion had died down, attention was swiftly directed to the countdown with Big Ben on the wireless, followed by Auld Lang Syne and a rousing God Save the King! Marvellous.

AOB

May I remind you all that contraband on the premises is strictly forbidden. We believe a number of personnel have been smuggling in home-made hooch through the gates using the 'conga' then distributing it to individuals using the 'hokey-cokey'. If you engage in these dances we will be watching you.

MARRIAGE ANNOUNCEMENT

Congratulations to Sgt Ted Eggert and Pt. Rosemary Ted Eggert (née Bacon) on their nuptials. The couple met last Tuesday and were married the following Tuesday at St Godwin's Church in Thucking-on-the-Naise.

NEW YEAR'S RESOLUTIONS

Those wishing to publish their New Year's Resolutions for 1941 are -

    Pte Butris - Intends to learn how to do a butterfly crawl.
    Pte Chake - Intends to try carrots.
    Pte Almond - Intends to go to church every day.
    Pte Grang - Intends to give up smoking.
    Pte Hadaway - Intends to take up smoking.

Good luck to all!

Until next month. Let us not forget the essential and vitally important work we do here at Button House. I wish each and everyone of you a very happy and triumphant new year.

God Save the King!

Capt.

South Berkshire Infirmary
Manor House Road, Reading, Berkshire RG38 8PL
Tel: 0735 765987 Fax: 0735 765988

The Pat Butcher Show
~~THE MAURICE CLAWSON SHOW~~

DATE: Monday 13 July 1981
START: 1300
RUNNING TIME: 120 minutes
PRESENTER: ~~Maurice Clawson~~ *Pat Butcher*
PRODUCER: Ken Malcolm

JINGLE: The greatest DJ in the area! ~~MAURICE CLAWSON~~ PAT BUTCHER!

Intro:

Hello Listeners! Patients, Visitors, Doctors, Nurses, Orderlies and everyone else. It's Pat Butcher here, filling in for Maurice while he's on holiday.

He's not gone abroad, we're just doing each other a favour. I'm helping him with his radio show (and, I might add, fulfilling a lifetime ambition) while he is helping me with some repairs at my house. Quite why he needs four days to fit, sand and paint a couple of skirting boards is beyond me but he told me he really wants to take his time and enjoy it and he's more than happy for me to hold the fort while he gets his hands dirty. Cheers Maurice!

South Berkshire Infirmary
Manor House Road, Reading, Berkshire RG38 8PL
Tel: 0735 765987 Fax: 0735 765988

So here I am! Pat Butcher – with you all afternoon. Whether you've just been hauled from the womb, stirred from a coma or are having your tonsils out, it's an honour for me to be the first, last and everything in your ears, from now until 4.

Now for today's surprise where I get to choose a tune for an unsuspecting patient! This is for Julia Tong in C Ward. Now, Julia needs a new kidney. The poor lass has been through a terrible ordeal over the last few months and, just as things were starting to look brighter, she received the news yesterday that her prospective donor wasn't a perfect match. And so, with that devastating upset, she's back to square one, and awaiting another donor. Bless her little heart.

So this one's for you, Julia! The Rolling Stones with 'You Can't Always Get What You Want'.

if I <u>WIN</u>...

— Today, the good people of Wooton South have proven themselves to be thoughtful, astute and prudent, and I intend to reward the faith they continue to show in me with diligence, gumption and sweat. In fact, I plan to work harder than those girls on the corner of West Street! (pause for laughter) No, no - seriously though, we are cleaning that up.

— I would like to pay tribute to the other candidates, especially Martin Sturmer, who ran a clean, fair and respectful campaign. We may not always agree on politics, but his conviction and sense of fair-play are beyond reproach.

— I would also like to thank hemma and my entire backroom team, without whom I would not be standing here for every long hour I put in, it felt like they put in two, and im sure they will sleep soundly in their beds tonight, safe in the knowledge of a job well done.

— But above all, I would like to thank my family. It is said that behind every great man is a great woman, and that is certainly true of my dear wife Margot, who could not have supported me more. well, all those nights I was away campaigning have been with it my love, as there will be a proud member in the bed tonight. And also, I won the election! (pause fo <u>BIG LAUGHTER</u>) But for now, let us pop some corks and slap some backs, for sanity is alive and well and living in Wooton South! Thank you - Thank you all!!

if I _LOSE_...

- Today, the people of Wooton South have proven themselves to be short-sighted, naive and dull-witted. Despite my tireless devotion to public service over the past four years, they have decided to recklessly roll the dice on a candidate with _no_ track record, on the strength of spurious promises and perhaps even bribery - who knows?

— The fact is that Martin Sturmer is a communist - pure + simple who has conducted an underhand campaign, rife with corruption and _dirty tricks_. He identified the seam of guileless gullibility that runs through this parish and exploited it for his own ends. And he knows full well that, on a level playing field in a more cogitative electorate, I would have wiped the floor with him, and then mopped it over with that ridiculous wig.

- Whilst I would dearly love to personally shoulder the responsibility for this defeat, as any good Englishman should, the fact is that I have been badly let down by my own campaign office. Where there should have been diligence, I found only disinterest. Where I would hope to see gumption, I found only gawping. For every hour they put in, I was giving _two_, and we can only now dream about the result we could have achieved had my work ethic been more prevalent in the backroom.

— Perhaps, if it were not for the incessant demands of family life, I could have found enough hours in the day to personally engineer a triumph, despite the many obstacles ranged against me. And I shall of course be speaking to my wife and daughter about how they could better support me going forward. For, rest assured, this will _not_ be the end for Julian Fawcett. I will be back on the hustings in four years time, by which point I hope you will have all learned your lesson! Good luck - you're going to need it.

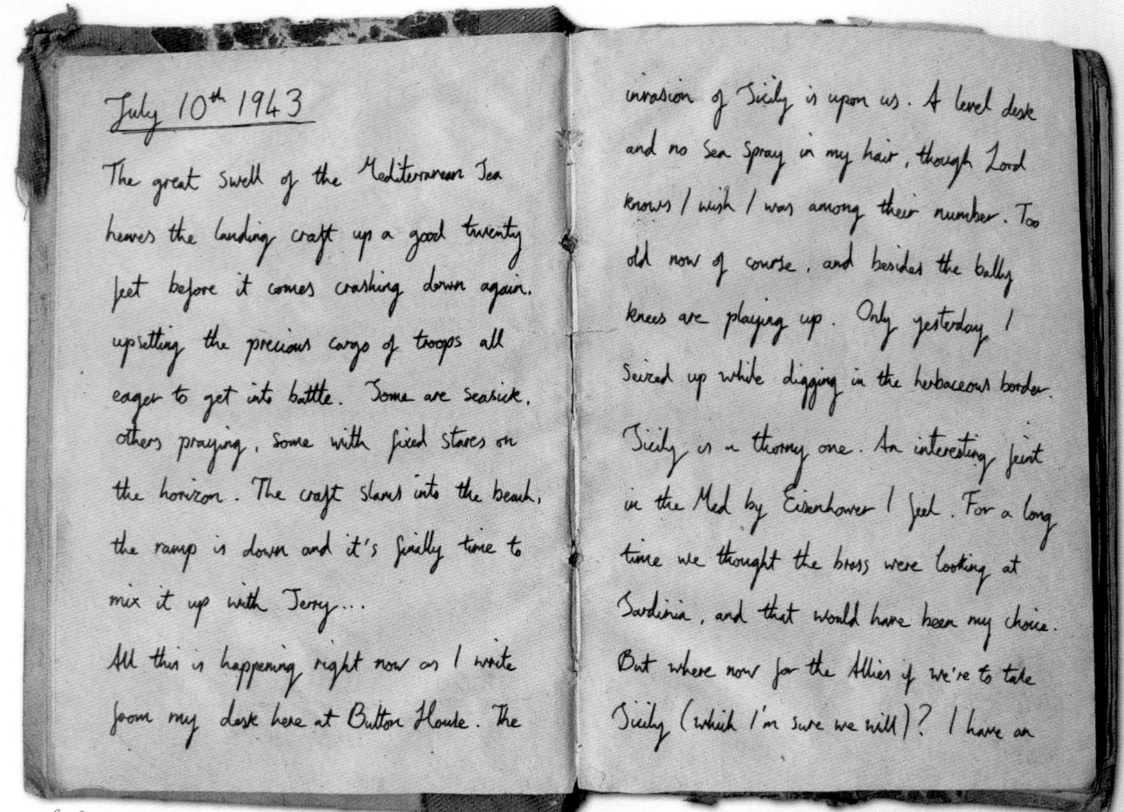

July 10th 1943

The great swell of the Mediterranean Sea heaves the landing craft up a good twenty feet before it comes crashing down again, upsetting the precious cargo of troops all eager to get into battle. Some are seasick, others praying, some with fixed stares on the horizon. The craft slams into the beach, the ramp is down and it's finally time to mix it up with Jerry...

All this is happening right now as I write from my desk here at Button House. The invasion of Sicily is upon us. A level desk and no sea spray in my hair, though Lord knows I wish I was among their number. Too old now of course, and besides the bally knees are playing up. Only yesterday I seized up while digging in the herbaceous border.

Sicily is a thorny one. An interesting feint in the Med by Eisenhower I feel. For a long time we thought the brass were looking at Sardinia, and that would have been my choice. But where now for the Allies if we're to take Sicily (which I'm sure we will)? I have an inkling that Italy will be next on the cards. But I feel very strongly that this might be a mistake. Hitler will be expecting that. Instead have we looked closely enough at Norway? I know we've been here before, but what about it? While Jerry is preoccupied, why not gather our forces and pour in through the top like hot oil?

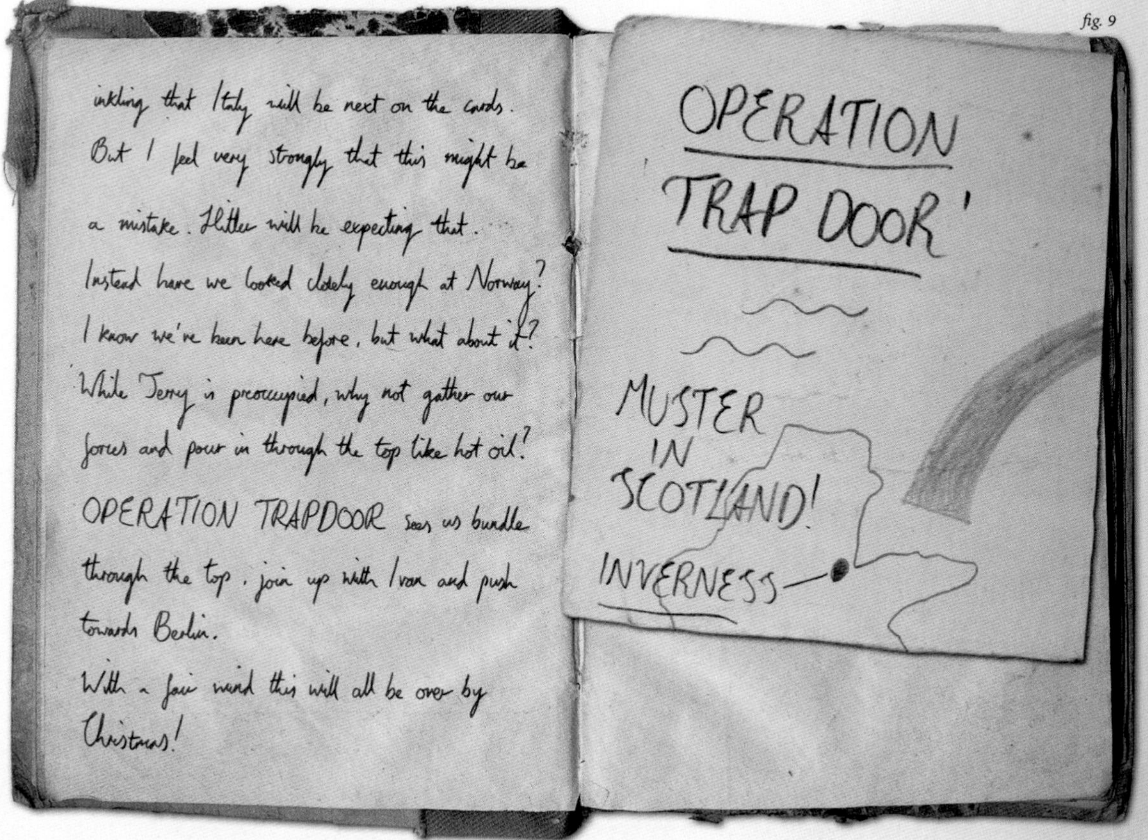

OPERATION TRAPDOOR sees us bundle through the top, join up with Ivan and push towards Berlin.

With a fair wind this will all be over by Christmas!

fig. 8

fig. 9

OPERATION TRAP DOOR

~~~~

MUSTER IN SCOTLAND!

INVERNESS —

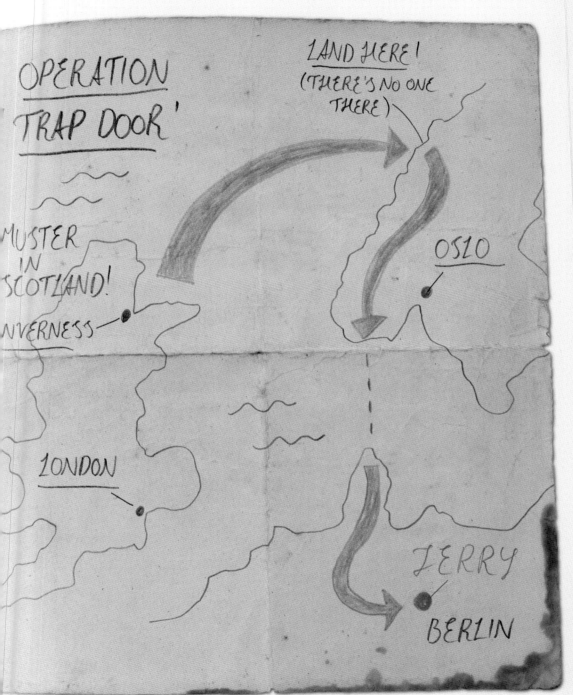

fig. 10

"Not just a
pretty face. . .
well, I am."

HUMPHREY

NAME

HUMPHREY

WHERE WERE YOU BORN?

In my father's house. Well, one of them. Richmond maybe? Apparently there was great fanfare. Literally, he'd hired a bugler. It was a boy you see. 'Carry on the line' and all that. Happiest day of his life he used to say. 'And you've been a crushing disappointment every moment since', he would joke. Very funny man, my father.

HOW DID YOU DIE?

Catholic plot. Not mine, but ... well, you know how these things go. The Queen's men burst in and ... let's just say I died by the sword.

FAVOURITE FOOD?

That's a toughie. I've had some real delicacies in my time. My father was a firm advocate of something stuffed inside something else. One time he had Cook put a swan in a porpoise. Sprained her wrist. Sparrow in a woodcock in a duck in a heron was quite nice, as I recall. Awful lot of bones though.

FAVOURITE DRINK?

Wine. Anything with a full body. (Laughed.) Imagine having a full body! (Looked into the distance for a really long time.)

FAVOURITE SONG?

My father claimed he wrote 'Greensleeves', but then he also claimed he invented jam, so it's hard to know what is entirely factual. Nice little ditty. Though, all things being equal, it's hard to beat the theme from Ski Sunday.

FAVOURITE SPORT?

There was a very popular one where a group of dogs tried to kill a chained bear. No one came out of that well - dogs, bears, people. All things being equal, it's hard to beat Ski Sunday.

BIGGEST REGRET?

Ehhhmm... I made some bad interior-design choices. A few ornaments I should have moved. Or, at least, secured better.

FONDEST MEMORY?

Probably the day I met my wife. We went riding in the Great Park, had a lunch of cold cuts by the river and fished until the sun set. And then I went to meet my wife.

WORST TRAIT?

I can be a bit of a chatterbox. My wife was always saying I'd 'run my voice' too much. At least, I think that's what she was saying? ('Tu as ruiné ma vie.') Sometimes when I wasn't even talking.

ANY WORDS OF WISDOM?

'Don't take advice from a man who got his head cut off.' (Laughed and then stared into the distance for a really long time again.)

As your MP and representative in government I will...

LOWER TAXES!
That means more money in YOUR pocket. Why give your money to the government? We don't need it. You do. Paying less tax means you get richer. So let's get richer together.

INTRODUCE THE TWO-CAR PLEDGE!
I believe every family deserves more than one car, whether you need it or not.

BRING BACK OIL TANKS FOR HOMES!
Oil is cheaper and more efficient. I believe, as so many of us do, that burning refined oil is a much better way of heating your home.

BAN THE UNION
Do you need a nurse to treat that wound? Well, TOUGH, she's o strike! Unions mean that people can go o strike when they wan Because they're now paid so much they d even NEED to work. come on, Let's get ri of unions forever.

RAISE THE NATIONAL SPEED LIMIT!
Do you know that we could all be getting t places much sooner? firmly believe everyor drives too slowly. On the open road it's perfectly safe to get to 100mph. But, in an abundance of caution let's say 90mph is fine Don't be a numpty, let's get it to 90!

KEEP IT FAWCETT. KEEP IT CONSERVATIV

VOTE CONSERVA

It does, will and trickle down

CO

150

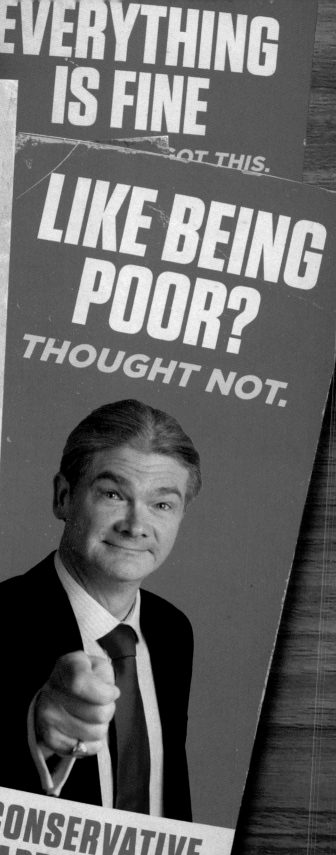

EVERYTHING IS FINE

...OT THIS.

LIKE BEING POOR?

THOUGHT NOT.

The REDS are STILL under the bed. The Labour Party will...

 MAKE HEALTH CARE UNIVERSAL!
If you want to tell a doctor how YOU want to be treated you should be able to. When you pay for it you can. Our government will give you that choice.

CHOICE! CHOICE! CHOICE!

 BAN PRIVATE SCHOOLS!
Why should anyone tell me where I should educate my children? If I want to pay for it I will and so can you and you should. Don't let them steal your right to choose.

CHOOSE! CHOOSE! CHOOSE!

 KEEP THE RAILWAYS NATIONALISED!
Why would we do this when splitting the railway system up into small pieces and making it a private enterprise, offering some to large foreign companies that YOU can invest in, will LOWER the fares and make booking a trip, even at short notice, affordable and simple? Regardless of which regional franchise you've chosen.

CHOSEN! CHOSEN! CHOSEN!

Conservative!
Conservative!
Conservative!

VOTE CONSERVATIVE
ON APRIL 9TH

OTE
ERVATIVE

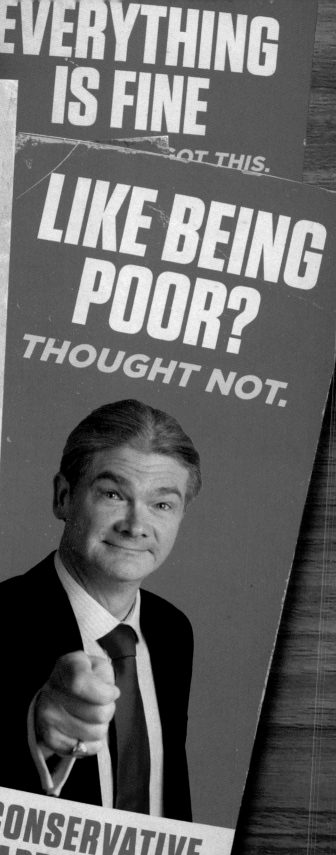

HERTS AND BEDS REGIMENT
BUTTON HOUSE HQ

*******SECRET*******

SERIES 3 Periodic Report

Annexe No. 2   HQ: 914 Button Ho. HQ 3 Coy (Int.)
AFTER ACTION REPORT   From: 0600 3rd Sept
3rd - 4th Sept 1940   To: 0600 4th Sept

    1. LOCATION: 3 Company HQ (Special Measures/Intelligence) (857432)

    2. LOCATION OF BATTALION
    See overlay.

    3. INTELLIGENCE OF HOSTILE INTENT
    Possible air attack.

    4. SUMMARY
    Recovery of Enemy Pilot.

SUMMARY

On the 3rd September report of aerial combat above 3 Company HQ (Int.) located at Button
House (HQ 3 Coy Int 857432).

A brief exchange after action with the Station Commander Group Captain Aitchison at
RAF Dunham Marsh confirms aerial skirmish at 0635 hours in exchange with Luftwaffe
bomber group and escort heading to London. Flt Lt Voles was sent to intercept.

REPORT

I awoke at 0615 hours to hear the roar of a Spitfire flying low over the roof here at
Button House. I thought perhaps it was another low-level practice run that the RAF have
been conducting in the area for the last three months.

COMPLAINT lodged twice with local area command RAF 11 Group (Southern Region) 5th May
1940 and 18th May 1940 — no response to date.

This time the low-level pass was justified as I noticed the Spitfire was trying to get
under a German aircraft that was wheeling around the house at high speed and at only
500 feet (or 'angels 500' as the RAF boys have it). I immediately identified the enemy as
a Messerschmitt Bf 109!

Initially I thought the 109 was attacking the house and I called for Sgt Foster to
alert the company to 'stand to! Sgt Foster sounded the alarm and the company began
to present itself in full readiness. I say began because there are still some teething
problems with our 'stand to' procedures and the company's subsequent readiness left
a lot to be desired. I am determined to iron this out in the fullness of time. I will
say there are still some who drag their feet. I know a lot of them have only just been
conscripted and they see this as a 'soft' posting but I do drill into them that the

Germans could invade at ANY TIME and WITHOUT WARNING. To this end I have been giving them a lecture entitled 'Jerry in The Woods', which asks the men and women here to think of the Germans waiting just inside the tree line ALL THE TIME and preparing to attack Button House at any moment. I am convinced it will help improve the response time should we need to defend our boundary.

Events were moving rapidly, you understand, and there was much confusion in the house. The Spitfire, piloted by Flt Lt Voles, performed a barrel roll over the house (very nearly clipping the highest chimney).

[COMPLAINT lodged of DANGEROUS FLYING to HQ 11 Group (Southern Command) 5 Sept 1940.]

I saw a black trail of smoke from the tail of the 109! She was going down! Due north of Button House into Maitland Wood [map of location on overlay]. I spotted the canopy of a parachute. No time to delay! I raced to the back exit of the house and straight to the path through the orchard to the woods.

Slow-going through the undergrowth but I took a heading from my last sighting of the parachute. Sure enough I found the parachute snagged in a tree in a clearing we call the Glade - a perfect spot for shaded bathing during the summer.

And standing next to the pond, a rather dazed German pilot! I don't know who was more stunned, me or him. It's true what they say about Jerry! This fellow looked like he'd stepped out of one of their posters! Quite the Aryan, I thought. I was reminded somewhat of a trip to Greece before the war, the statues and so on. A shock of blond hair and tall, yet quite shaken after his air battle. But here was the enemy and he was now in my backyard! Time to act! Below I have tried to recall our initial exchange as accurately as possible:

Me: "I say! Are you German?"
Pilot: "[GERMAN WORDS]"
Me: "Of course you're German, you've just bailed out!"
Pilot: "[MORE GERMAN WORDS]" (Perhaps something about the sky - he was pointing upwards a lot)
Me: "Yes. Those RAF lot have given you a jolly good hiding I can see. Understand that you are now under arrest! You have been captured!"

It was then I realised I was still in my dressing gown. In the confusion I had neglected to get dressed. I couldn't possibly detain him without my uniform on! It might possibly be a breach of the Geneva Convention or at the very least, etiquette. Here was a fellow officer after all. So I commanded him to stay put, I would be back presently. He looked mildly baffled and even waved as I left.

I raced back to Button House and got changed. When I made it back to the Glade in full uniform he was nowhere to be seen. The villain! I mean, what has happened to the world when an officer cannot keep his word? I know he's German but still! When he's captured he should be reminded that his conduct was unbecoming of an officer and a gentleman.

Despite being fit (he was one of the fittest young men I'd seen in a while - not sure what they're feeding them over there but it's clearly working) and I'm sure very capable (not to mention having extraordinary stamina), I'm certain he won't get far.

The rest of the day I detailed ten men to comb the area up to the boundary and beyond into Beckett's Wood. There was no sign of the young Luftwaffe pilot but I'm confident he will get picked up in the next day or so.

Signed: Captain

14th September 1779

Whose writing is this?
The Queen's!
I beg your pardon?
Yes, you read it correctly, I am the Queen... of Hide-and-Go-Seek! That's me! Don't worry, I'm not an actual Queen. Imagine!

I merely mean to express what a stupendous job I did of playing hide-and-go-seek with Eleanor today. I don't know what has changed, I always used to be very bad at it when we played it together with Mother and Father. I was too giggly and clumsy and Eleanor was sly as a fox. I still loved playing, though. This morning it was actually Eleanor's idea to play, and before we had even had breakfast at that! She hid first and, unbelievably, I found her in no time. Almost as soon as I had left the bedroom I heard her say, "Oh boo, you found me!" Poor thing. Then she said, "Oh well, now you hide! And remember you can use the whole grounds!"

Well, I knew at once that I should hide outside so I ran to the gardens. I looked all around and was quite overwhelmed for choice. I decided to crouch behind Florence, the statue and, good heavens, what a splendid choice she was! I don't think I've ever stayed in one place for so long before. I entertained myself talking to Florence and watching the bees buzzing round the flowers. When the sun was high in the sky I started to feel quite hungry and thirsty. Luckily there was some rainwater caught in Florence's hand so I drank that like a cat.

Kitty! Meow! The hunger was less easily solved but I didn't want to give up my first chance at really winning hide-and-go-seek so every time my tummy rumbled I said, "Keep it to yourself, you greedy thing!" I'm not sure when I had the wonderful idea to eat my purse but I think it was getting dark by then. I only nibbled a corner of it, at the top so that it wouldn't make a hole in the bottom for my coins to fall through. It didn't taste very delicious but I think it tricked my tummy. Later, I finally heard footsteps outside. I tried my very best to keep quiet but I was so excited I couldn't help but let out a little laugh. It turned out not to be Eleanor, but Perigrave, the footman. He insisted that I had to come inside as father would begin to worry, so I followed him back into the house. Well, poor Eleanor was sitting by the fire, reading. She had quite forgotten about our game and missed out on all the fun, the dear thing! I felt simply awful for her as she had apparently spent most of the day with a boring boy who was visiting on his mother's instruction to 'make acquaintance with the Higham girls'. She said I was very lucky that I had not had to sit with him because I wouldn't have liked him and that I was the Queen of Hide-and-Go-Seek.

So All Hail the Queen!

South Berkshire Infirmary

Manor House Road, Reading, Berkshire RG38 8PL
Tel: 0735 765987 Fax: 0735 765988

The Pat Butcher Show
~~THE MAURICE CLAWSON SHOW~~

DATE: Monday 20 July 1981
START: 1300
RUNNING TIME: 120 minutes

PRESENTER: ~~Maurice Clawson~~ Pat Butcher
PRODUCER: Ken Malcolm

JINGLE: The greatest DJ in the area! ~~MAURICE CLAWSON~~ PAT BUTCHER

Intro:

Hello Listeners, Patients, Visitors, Doctors, Nurses, Orderlies and everyone else!

It's DJ Pat Butcher here, filling in once again for my mate Maurice Clawson. Unfortunately Maurice is feeling a bit under the weather this week with a rather nasty case of man flu. Luckily for him my wife Carol, who is a cracking cook, is popping in to visit him every day with some excellent homemade dinners! Including her pièce de resistance (French) a very moreish hot pot.

Maurice actually gave me a message to share with you all that says, "Send my best to my listeners and tell them please not to worry about me because I've got Carol playing nurse and she has a heavenly bedside manner."

She certainly does. Get well soon Maurice!

156

South Berkshire Infirmary

Manor House Road, Reading, Berkshire RG38 8PL
Tel: 0735 765987 Fax: 0735 765988

Talking dinners, Carol has put me on a diet! We've got a wedding coming up and I can't get into my three-piece. Now listening, I've never dieted before and a lot of people have told me I'd struggle and that before long, the cravings would be too much to bear and all I'd be thinking about was food. Well, let me tell you, I'm now on day 2 and it's easy as pie, a piece of cake, like taking sweets from a baby!

It's just a simple question of mind over matter.

Anyway, here's Dee Dee Sharp with 'Mash Potato Time'.

Today's playlist:

Booker T and the MGs – Green Onions
The Beach Boys – Wild Honey
Millie Small – My Boy Lollipop
10cc – Life is a Minestrone
Don McLean – American Pie
The Beatles – Savoy Truffle
The Archies – Sugar Sugar
Grateful Dead – Cream Puff War
The Strangeloves – I Want Candy
Micheal Bolton – The Hunger

"If I could touch
you lot, I'd kill you!
If I could see you!
And you weren't dead!"

MIKE

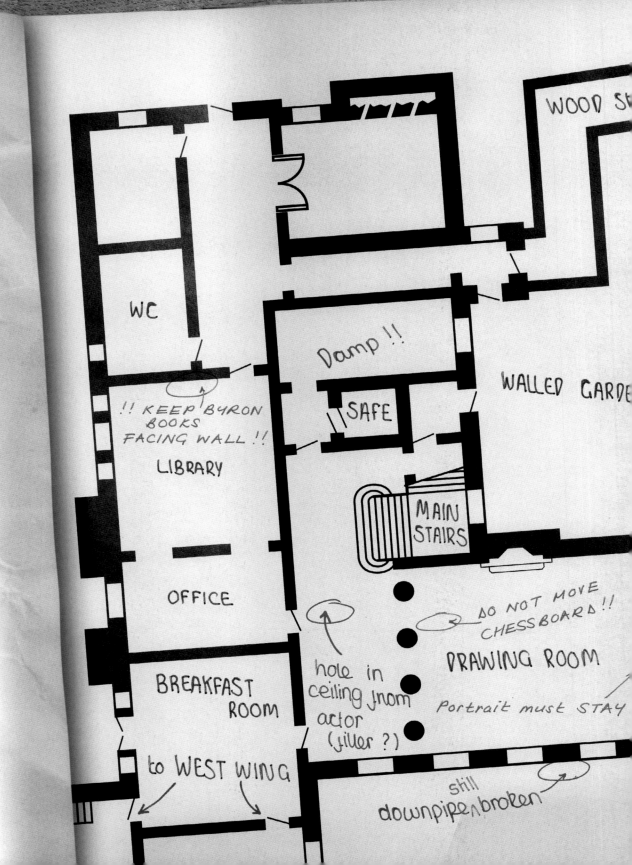

WOOD ST

WC

Damp !!

WALLED GARDE

!! KEEP BYRON BOOKS FACING WALL !!

SAFE

LIBRARY

MAIN STAIRS

OFFICE

DO NOT MOVE CHESSBOARD !!

hole in ceiling from actor (filler ?)

DRAWING ROOM

BREAKFAST ROOM

Portrait must STAY

to WEST WING

still downpipe broken

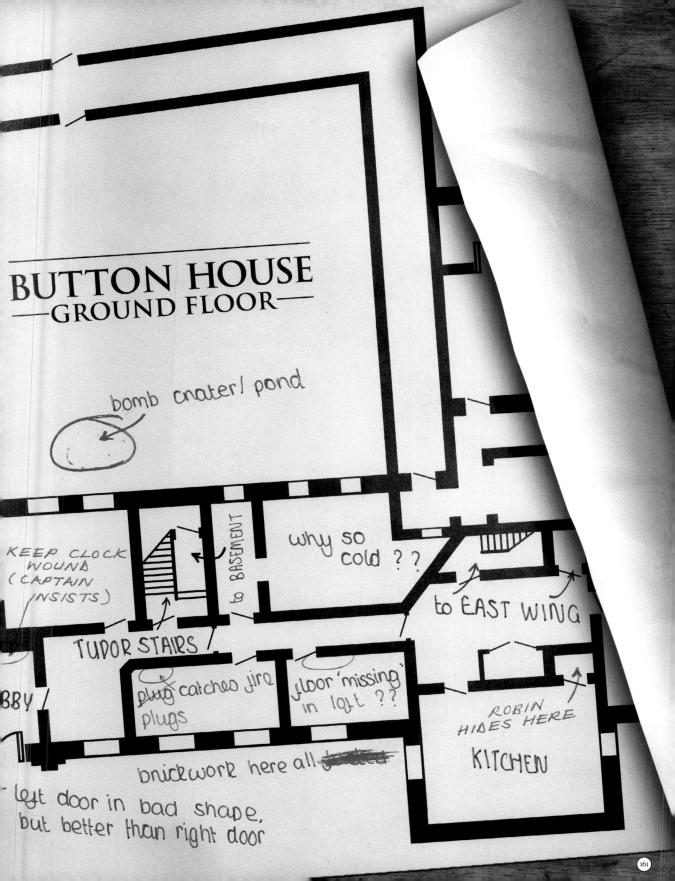

BUTTON HOUSE
—GROUND FLOOR—

bomb crater/ pond

KEEP CLOCK
WOUND
(CAPTAIN
INSISTS)

to BASEMENT

why so
cold ??

to EAST WING

TUDOR STAIRS

plug catches fire
plugs

floor 'missing'
in loft ??

ROBIN
HIDES HERE

KITCHEN

BBY

brickwork here all ~~demolished~~

left door in bad shape,
but better than right door

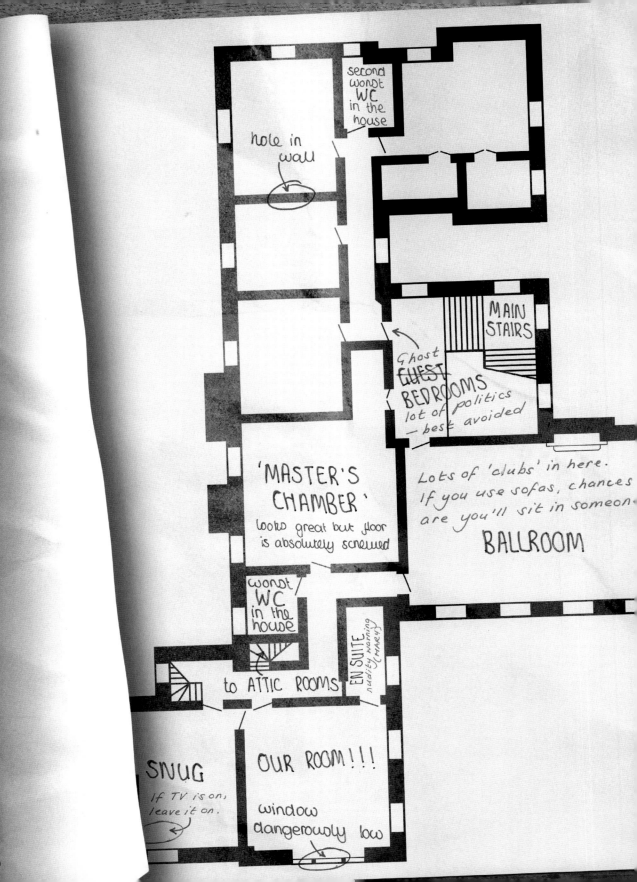

BUTTON HOUSE
FIRST FLOOR

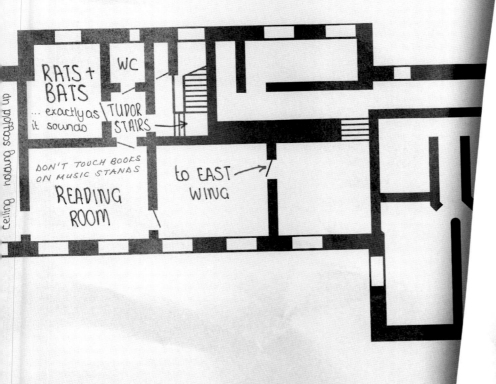

ceiling holding scaffold up

RATS +
BATS
...exactly as
it sounds

WC

TUDOR
STAIRS

DON'T TOUCH BOOKS
ON MUSIC STANDS

READING
ROOM

to EAST
WING

++++++SECRET++++++   HQ 3 Coy Int. Button House
                       HEMEL HEMPSTEAD/(857432)

DATE: 28th February 1940
Issue N°5/8

MUNITIONS REQUEST

++++URGENT++++

ATTENTION:
Lieutenant General Sir Bertie Drew FISHER, K.C.B., C.M.G., D.S.O.
HQ Southern Command

FROM:
Officer Commanding HQ 3 Coy (Int.)

Sir,

Many thanks for your response to my recent request.

I must say I am disappointed with the last response from your ADC, Captain
Chetterton-Pillar. I don't think he realises the urgency that surrounds my request.

A week ago at Button House we believed our perimeter to have been breached by the
enemy. Cpl Bottlesby and the guard contingent at the time were startled in the night
and Bottlesby discharged his requisitioned weapon (a shotgun).

Upon investigation it was discovered that it was in fact not a German paratrooper,
but a fox that had got in amongst the bins. I have reprimanded the Corporal but that
leaves us with one damp shell for the shotgun.

Are we to defend ourselves with nothing more than cricket bats?

I would urge you to reconsider my request.

Yours in anticipation,

OFFICER COMMANDING HQ 3 Coy (Int.) Button House

Captain

Office of Lieutenant General Sir Bertie Drew FISHER, K.C.B., C.M.G., D.S.O.

HQ SOUTHERN COMMAND

++++++SECRET++++++

The Office of
Lieutenant General Sir Bertie Drew FISHER, K.C.B., C.M.G., D.S.O.
HQ Southern Command

Captain Oliver Chetterton-Pillar ADC

MUNITIONS REQUEST

++++URGENT++++

ATTENTION:
Officer Commanding
HQ 3 Coy (Int.) Button House/HEMEL HEMPSTEAD/(857432)
DATE: 2nd April 1940
Issue N°2/3

FROM:
Captain Oliver CHETTERTON-PILLAR - ADC to Lt Gen. FISHER (Southern Command).

Sir,

I respectfully ask you to address any future correspondence to me.

To be clear, your letters to the General have to come through my office first and you may rest assured that I will deal with all requests on his behalf.

I am sorry to hear that your Corporal has discharged his weapon accidentally. This happens in war, particularly as the country is in such a state of readiness and nerves are running high.

It is with regret that I must inform you the General's decision remains final as we are fighting a rearguard action in France and his energies are required elsewhere.

This is the final decision on the matter.

Regards,

Captain Oliver Chetterton-Pillar, Coldstream Guards.

"Well, we didn't
win the war with
attitudes like that."

CAPTAIN

NAME THE CAPTAIN

WHERE WERE YOU BORN?

Bledlow. Well, technically on the boundary with Kingston Stert, but within the civil parish of Bledlow-cum-Saunderton, Buckinghamshire, England. WSW of Princes Risborough, but on the Chinnor side. I believe it's now in the Hotel Papa postal area, but they're a little after my time, so I cannot be sure of the suffix. You must forgive me for being so vague.

HOW DID YOU DIE?

Well I couldn't possibly say. I was in uniform at the time you see and it's therefore off limits. Classified. All very hush hush, you see.

FAVOURITE FOOD?

meat and two veg.

FAVOURITE DRINK?

Very partial to a bitter shandy.

FAVOURITE SONG?

'In the Mood' by Glenn Miller. You know, the version about the daddy with the beautiful eyes.

FAVOURITE SPORT?

Cricket. Always cricket. Sport of kings. The king of sport.

BIGGEST REGRET?

Arriving at the front in 1918 just as the armistice sounded. Didn't even so much as peek over the top.

FONDEST MEMORY?

Meeting Lord Brigadier Sir Anthony Bartholomew Raisinby Jones. Splendid fellow. And, look, my time at Button House, well it was a veritable buffet of wonderful moments. One in particular stands out actually, a Sunday afternoon stroll with, er, a very special er... actually look, it's all a matter of wartime records you see, so that's classified I'm afraid. I'm not at liberty to divulge that particular moment so... yes coming back to your question, it was meeting Sir Anthony Bartholomew Raisinby Jones. Yes. Thank you.

WORST TRAIT?

Ah well, I'm a bit of a sloucher I'm afraid. Uniform hides it a little, but my shoulders naturally drop a full inch forward of the hips. Two if I'm tired. I try to keep my trapezius engaged at all times, but I'm sure I once heard some muttering in the mess as I leant forward to ladle the carrots. I shall redouble my efforts. Don't want to get a reputation as some sort of slovenly wastrel.

ANY WORDS OF WISDOM?

Keep your chin up, your bat straight, and your whistle clean.

SEX PEST MP

TORY
SC

Julian Fawcett MP
Member of Parliament for Wooton South

SHRE

HOUSE OF COMMONS

SHRED

CORRECTIONS & CLARIFICATIONS

Following correspondence with the office of Mr Julian Fawcett MP, in reference to our front page story of 12 May ('ALL ARMS AND LEGS: Honey trap hooker snags gun deal MP') we are happy to concede the following errors and correct the record accordingly:

- The car in which Mr Fawcett first entertained Miss Grey was a silver Daimler, not a silver Rolls-Royce.

- The birthmark was on the upper portion of the left buttock and not the lower back, as initially reported.

- The phrase "cocktail of party drugs" was technically inaccurate, as the substances were taken in sequence and not as a mixture, as the term "cocktail" connotes.

- Mr Fawcett did not "put on" the bra, as the clasp was never fully fastened.

- In keeping with our style guide, the fourth hotel guest should have been described as a "Sheikh" (British English) and not a "Sheik" (American English). As such we are happy to amend the relevant line to read: "Fawcett then handed the rolled-up note to the Sheikh saying, 'Have a toot on that, Ali my boy!'"

- The Javelin K-24 is a "surface-to-air" missile, not an "air-to-surface" missile.

- The threatening voicemail our reporter received addressed him as a "f***ing t***ser" and not a "bl**dy w***ker".

The other 137 complaints received were rejected as contrary to recorded facts. We would like to take this opportunity to wish Mr Fawcett well in his next career steps.

170

JULIAN FERDINAND FAWCETT

**Julian Ferdinand Fawcett MP,
Conservative politician and cabinet minister,
died March 18. He was born on May 9, 1945.**

Julian Fawcett, MP, who has died aged 48, was one of the more colourful characters in modern British politics, with a varied career that encompassed front-bench, back-bench and numerous off-bench roles – many of them concurrent. Whilst he became known for his work in journalism, finance, media, armaments and pharmaceuticals – not to mention his tireless commitment to consultancy – it was serving his constituents that really fired his enthusiasm. "No politician in living memory has represented as many different constituencies as I have," he once told the Guardian, "and to suggest that's the result of fleeing scandal, rather than a heartfelt desire to meet and help more people, would be the very embodiment of cynicism."

One of the staff at his constituency office remained stoic while paying tribute to Fawcett's work ethic, saying, "You would sometimes see him here." Another spoke of his willingness to engage with a wide variety of correspondence: "It just piled up on his desk," they said.

Never afraid to speak his mind, Fawcett strongly believed that holding people to account should not just be confined to the powerful, spearheading such bold initiatives as 'Are You REALLY Homeless?' and 'Shop a Scrounger, Win a Lounger'. His robust views on such issues as crime, taxation and women are also well documented. And his 'A Dog is Just For Christmas' campaign, whilst successfully addressing overcrowding in animal shelters, was condemned by animal-welfare charities as "short-sighted".

But it was the issue of Europe that became his greatest passion. His early reputation was formed around his tireless campaigning to join Europe – a topic that followed him through his time in office, as he variously campaigned for closer ties to Europe, looser ties to Europe, to stay in Europe and to leave Europe. Certainly his opponents were quick to seize on his "schizophrenic whims", but Fawcett always denied that his financial links to trade bodies on both sides of the channel were the root of his drifting opinion.

"It is so important that we retain the ability to have our minds changed, and I will always believe that, regardless of what anyone says."

Despite his reputation as a shrewd political operator, those who worked closely with him often spoke warmly of his human touch, citing his ribald anecdotes and "fruity" jokes. And his commitment to

encouraging fresh blood within the party was a source of great personal pride. He certainly forged close friendships with many young colleagues and interns, often working late into the night in his London flat.

He was a committed family man and a staunch believer in what he called "old-fashioned values", with his refrain of "Family! Family! Family!" becoming a party battle cry during last year's conference. And he was steadfast in his desire to protect his own family from the thrust and parry of Westminster life, encouraging his wife to embrace country living. "She's better off away from all the stress and long hours," he once said in an interview. "She doesn't want to see me down here, hammering away night after night."

The exact details of his death are yet to be confirmed by the coroner, but the fact he was attending a party fundraiser suggests he went out doing what he loved.

He is survived by his wife, daughter and some other children.

Not again!

Ford Transit
ARIES

TAURUS

BUM!

LEO

Dead Snake

VIRGO

TAXI!
CAPRICORNUS

some sort bird?

Balloon

SAGITTARIUS

ROBIN'S
ZODIA

GEMINI

MOONAH !
(not actual
Moonah)

CANCER

ARGHHHHHH !

Captain Stick

more star
this way

(Mary)

SCORPIUS

no star here

AQUARIUS

Hey, that
MY taxi !

PISCES
It's me

CONSTELLATIONS

Portraits of Lady Stephanie Button (1854–1912)

Lady Stephanie Button (née Colebrooke) was born in London into relative wealth, her father, Simeon Colebrooke, having made his fortune from importing tea and rare artifacts that could be hidden in tea. However, a combination of addiction and superstition (he would only bet on horses with certain birthstones) led Simeon to the verge of bankruptcy, necessitating a 'love match' between Stephanie and George Button, heir to the Higham textile fortune. The marriage, which she described as 'most tolerable', ended in tragedy when Stephanie fell from a first floor window. Stricken with grief, George never remarried, ending his days in the house with only his staff for company.

ABOVE:
Stephanie Colebrooke
Carbon Print, *c.*1876

LEFT:
Lady Stephanie Button
Bromide Print, *c.*1910

RIGHT:
Lady Stephanie Button and Dante
Oil on canvas, 1893

Loaned to the Hertfordshire Historical Society by Alison Cooper

ABOVE:

Needlecraft Sampler by Stephanie Button
Cotton and Wool on Monk's Cloth, 1909

This Edwardian 'sampler' reflects the passions and beliefs of the maker. The animals depicted are thought to be departed family pets: Dante, Lady Button's devoted Papillon, and her favourite horse, Montague, about whom little is known beyond his birthstone (amethyst).

fig. 11

Photograph of an unknown soldier found in
the Commanding Officer's belongings after
Button House was decommissioned at the end
of the Second World War.

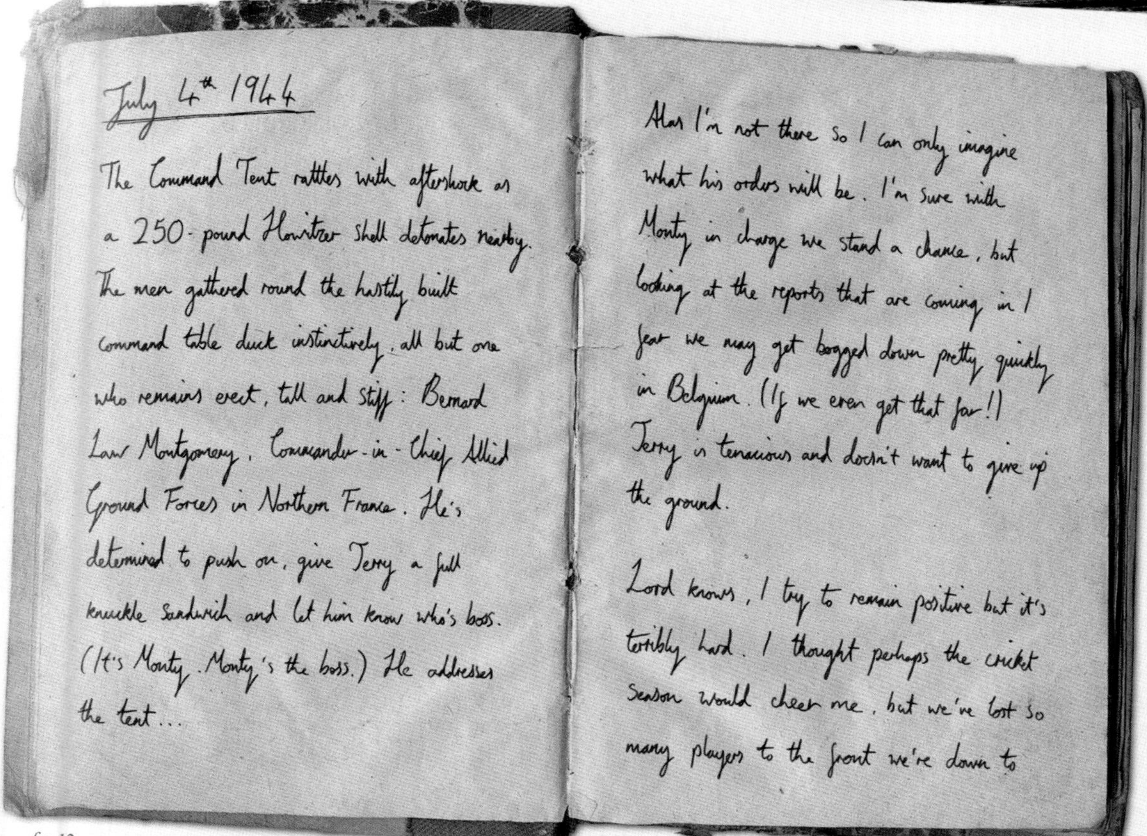

July 4th 1944

The Command Tent rattles with aftershock as a 250-pound Howitzer shell detonates nearby. The men gathered round the hastily built command table duck instinctively, all but one who remains erect, tall and stiff: Bernard Law Montgomery, Commander-in-Chief Allied Ground Forces in Northern France. He's determined to push on, give Jerry a full knuckle sandwich and let him know who's boss. (It's Monty. Monty's the boss.) He addresses the tent...

Alas I'm not there so I can only imagine what his orders will be. I'm sure with Monty in charge we stand a chance, but looking at the reports that are coming in I fear we may get bogged down pretty quickly in Belgium. (If we even get that far!) Jerry is tenacious and doesn't want to give up the ground.

Lord knows, I try to remain positive but it's terribly hard. I thought perhaps the cricket season would cheer me, but we've lost so many players to the front we're down to

fig. 12

fig. 13

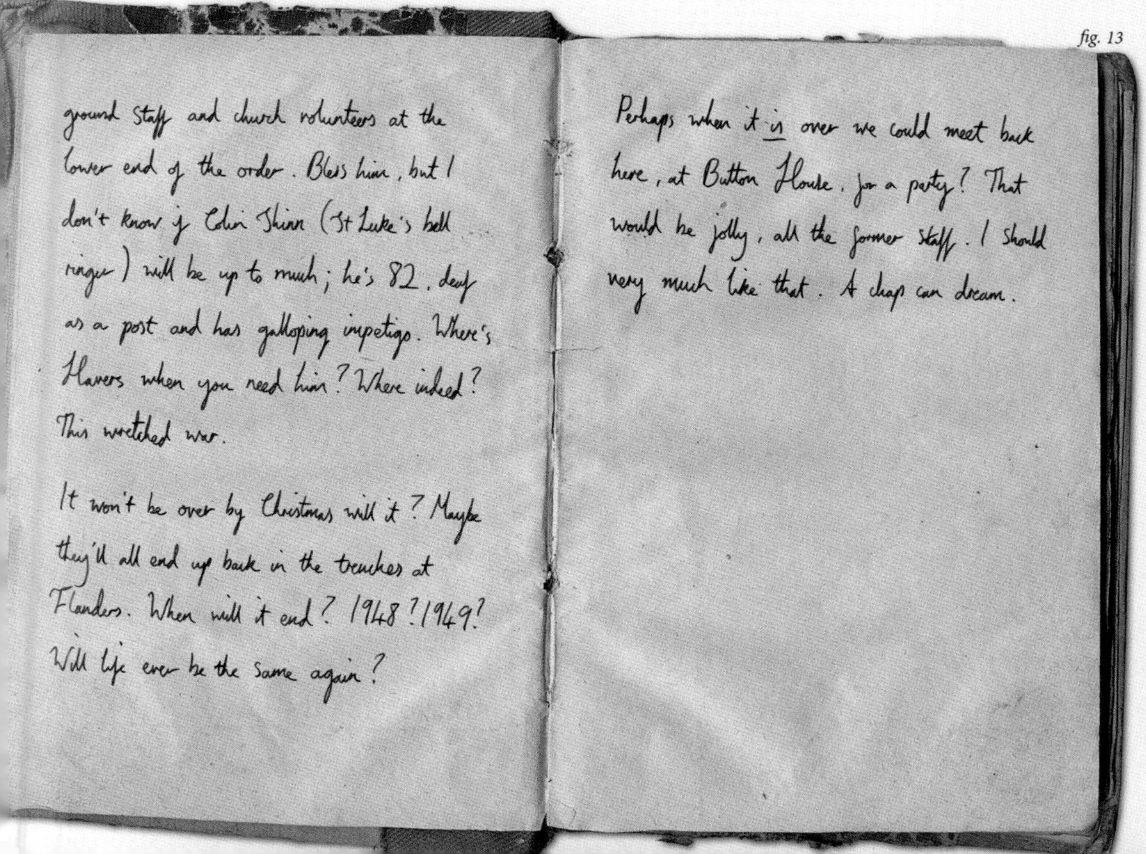

ground staff and church volunteers at the lower end of the order. Bless him, but I don't know if Colin Shinn (St Luke's bell ringer) will be up to much; he's 82, deaf as a post and has galloping impetigo. Where's Havers when you need him? Where indeed? This wretched war.

It won't be over by Christmas will it? Maybe they'll all end up back in the trenches at Flanders. When will it end? 1948? 1949? Will life ever be the same again?

Perhaps when it _is_ over we could meet back here, at Button House, for a party? That would be jolly, all the former staff. I should very much like that. A chap can dream.

The Tyger
William Blake

T.J.

Tyger, tyger, burning bright *Is the tiger on fire?*
In the forests of the night, *Are the forests of the night*
What immortal hand or eye *different to the forests of the day?*
Could frame thy fearful symmetry? *If eye rhymes with symmetry,*
I don't know why I waste my time labouring
over my verse at all.

In what distant deeps or skies
Burnt the fire of thine eyes? *Oh, just the eyes on fire, then?*
On what wings dare he aspire? *He's got wings now?!*
What the hand dare seize the fire? *Come to your senses, Blake!*

And what shoulder and what art *Boring! We have the idea now,*
Could twist the sinews of thy heart? *Blake, you like the tiger.*
And, when thy heart began to beat, *It's big and strong.*
What dread hand and what dread feet?

It's starting to feel as though his
What the hammer? what the chain? *admiration for this tyger is*
In what furnace was thy brain? *bordering on perversion.*
What the anvil? what dread grasp *It's a tiger, Blake, not a*
Dare its deadly terrors clasp? *woman!*

When the stars threw down their spears, *The stars have got*
And watered heaven with their tears, *spears, have they? What*
Did he smile his work to see? *has the moon got, a musket?*
Did he who made the lamb make thee?

Tyger, tyger, burning bright *I had not realised you were*
In the forests of the night, *allowed to just repeat the first*
What immortal hand or eye *verse at the end.*
Dare frame thy fearful symmetry? *Good to know.*

T.J.

When Bishop Berkeley said 'there was no matter,'

   And proved it—'twas no matter what he said: *repetition of matter*

They say his system 'tis in vain to batter;

   Too subtle for the airiest human head;   *batter, shatter, what next?*

And yet who can believe it? I would shatter

   Gladly all matters down to stone or lead,   *MATTER again!*

Or adamant, to find the world a spirit,   *Good Lord*

   And wear my head, denying that I wear it.   *What does this even mean? Are we really supposed to believe somebody is saying he is 'wearing' his head and he is*

What a sublime discovery 'twas to make the   *saying, "no sir, you are*

   Universe universal egotism!   *mistaking. I am not wearing*

That all 's ideal—all ourselves: I'll stake the   *my head!"*

   World (be it what you will) that that 's no schism.   *I am completely lost here.*

O Doubt!—if thou be'st Doubt, for which some take thee;   *And if I cannot understand*

   But which I doubt extremely—thou sole prism   *I hardly think the lady readers he so*

Of the Truth's rays, spoil not my draught of spirit!   *prizes shall!*

   Heaven's brandy, though our brain can hardly bear it.   *spirit and 'bear it' hardly rhyme, unless one forces it to by uttering 'spare-it', or alternatively 'beer it'*

For ever and anon comes Indigestion,   *Indigestion now!!! How poetic*

   (Not the most 'dainty Ariel') and perplexes   *George, why don't you write a*

Our soarings with another sort of question: *poem about cramp next, or the boil on your buttocks!*

   And that which after all my spirit vexes,

Is, that I find no spot where man can rest eye on,   *I mean, what is his twittering on about here? That there*

   Without confusion of the sorts and sexes,   *is nowhere one can look without*

Of beings, stars, and this unriddled wonder,   *finding questions of creation, of*

   The world, which at the worst 's a glorious blunder—   *of existence itself and our place in the world? Well, I suppose that is...*

This couplet is rather good to be fair to George.

Try saying that out loud George!

Dr C.A. COULDSON
Bsc, MB BS, MRCPath
Home Office Accredited Forensic Pathologist

Consultant – Forensic Pathology Services

FPS
Forensic Pathology Services

THIS IS A CONFIDENTIAL REPORT TO THE CORONER AND SHOULD NOT BE DISCLOSED TO A THIRD PARTY WITHOUT HIS PERMISSION

CONFIDENTIAL

POST MORTEM REPORT

SC: 135/1993/GK

<u>Julian Ferdinand FAWCETT, MP — date of birth: 9th May 1945</u>

On the morning of March 21st 1993 I attended the mortuary at Hemel Hempstead Hospital in order to undertake a post mortem examination on the body of Julian FAWCETT.

The post mortem examination commenced at 9:30 hrs.

Those persons present were:

Dr C Couldson   Pathologist
Dr S Dodds   Assistant Pathologist

Received in a black body bag, tagged: Fawcett, J <u>135/1993/GK</u>.

The deceased is wearing a pale pinstripe shirt, red and blue tie, navy suit jacket, black socks, black formal shoes and union flag sock suspenders. No other garments were present below the waist.

The body is a white male, measuring 6' 2" and weighing 13 stone 7 ounces — normally developed apart from slight muscular asymmetry and swelling of the right rotator cuff. (Golf?)

Superficial bite marks on the third finger of the left hand are consistent with the deceased's own teeth, mostly likely from an attempt to remove a tight wedding ring. A bite mark on the left buttock did not match the deceased's teeth however, but was deemed non-pertinent.

Minor abrasions and slight redness was observed on the deceased's knees, consistent with 2-3 minutes of light friction.

A suspected rash on the lower abdomen was subsequently identified by Dr Dodds as lipstick, most likely Chanel 'Cherry Passion'.

The corner of a foil prophylactic wrapper was found in the upper portion of the inter-gluteal cleft.

A white powdery residue was observed in a portion of facial stubble above the top lip. A sample has been sent to toxicology for identification.

Fingernails short. Dark, gritty substance ingrained under several nails ~~suggesting prolonged physical labour.~~
identified as caviar

INTERIOR EXAMINATION

OESOPHAGUS:	Of normal presentation for age and weight
STOMACH:	Of normal presentation for age and weight
INTESTINES:	Of normal presentation for age and weight
LUNGS:	Of normal presentation for age and weight
LIVER:	Yellow, pallid, enlarged, hardened, fatty
KIDNEYS:	Of normal presentation for age and weight
SPLEEN:	Of normal presentation for age and weight
ENDOCRINE ORGANS:	Of normal presentation for age and weight
HEART:	Enlarged, dilated, evidence of localised necrosis

TOXICOLOGY

The blood sample contained the drug Benzoylmethylecgonine at a concentration of ██████ micrograms per millilitre.

The blood sample contained the drug Methylenedioxymethamphetamine at a concentration of ██████ micrograms per millilitre.

The blood sample contained the drug phytocannabinoid tetrahydrocannabinol at a concentration of ██████ micrograms per millilitre.

The blood sample contained alcohol at a concentration of ██████ milligrams per 100 millilitres.

CONCLUSIONS

It is my professional opinion that Mr Fawcett's cause of death was:

1) Myocardial Infarction

A combination of substance abuse and sudden exertion are likely aggravating factors.

Dr C. A. Couldson
Bsc, MB BS, MRCPath
Home Office Accredited Forensic Pathologist

KITTY'S TOP TEN TRACKS

Kitty says that pretty much anything that comes on the radio is her new favourite song, so I tried to get her to narrow it down to just ten...

* SATURDAY NIGHT
by WHIGFIELD
I actually first heard this song on a Thursday morning but was able to overcome my confusion. My favourite bit is probably where she says 'da ba da dan dee dee dee da nee na nana', even though I was never schooled in that language.

* DON'T STOP MOVIN'
by S CLUB 7
Not only a mesmerising ditty, but also a very good moral. It really is ever so important to keep moving. Unless it's swimming and you've just eaten.

* I KNOW WHERE IT'S AT
by ALL SAINTS
I used to lose things all the time, so this song just feels very inspirational to me.

* 2 BECOME 1
by the SPICE GIRLS
They only actually say '2 become 1' in the bit before the chorus, not in the chorus itself, which is very clever. I imagine that was Victoria's idea, because she's the most sophisticated.

* SHAKE IT OFF
by TAYLOR SWIFT
Hands down my favourite song about cramp.

✳ I WANT TO HOLD YOUR HAND
by THE BEATLES
   I would very much like to hold a hand,
   Or a flower. Or a cup. I think I just
   generally miss holding things.
✳ HAPPY
by PHARRELL WILLIAMS
   Just a very happy song about being happy
   that makes me feel happy. I can
   completely see how it got its name. And
   there's a line about feeling like a room with
   no roof, which really reminds me of MY room
   following the great storm of 1987.
✳ ALL OF BEYONCÉ'S SONGS
by BEYONCÉ
   Because Beyoncé.
✳ WUTHERING HEIGHTS
by KATE BUSH
   Your KATHY. As in Katherine. As in KITTY!
   It's basically a song about me out on a
   wild and windy moor, which is so well
   observed, because I love a nice walk.
✳ I WANT TO DANCE WITH SOMEBODY
by WHITNEY HOUSTON
   I just really do.

185

"I should never
have given an
eight-year-old
a lethal weapon."

PAT

NAME PAT

WHERE WERE YOU BORN?

Huddersfield Royal Infirmary. Saturday 20th April 1946 at 4.40pm. Just in time for the scores! (We lost to Leeds.)

HOW DID YOU DIE?

Arrow in the neck and subsequent bus crash. It's a long story. Actually that's it.

FAVOURITE FOOD?

Now then. Let's get down to brass tacks. Are we talking about a speciality meal? Because if so, it's my all-time fave – Christmas dinner with all the trimmings. Desert island meal? Scotch broth, followed by beef stew, followed by tinned peaches (hydration is key). Or my last meal before execution? A Full English Breakfast Challenge (basically five Full English breakfasts). That will hopefully finish me off. Or my favourite snack? Scotch egg (nature's lunchbox).

FAVOURITE DRINK?

Pint of bitter. Or Vimto.

FAVOURITE SONG?

'Lovely Day' by Bill Withers.

FAVOURITE SPORT?

Footy! COME ON THE TOWN!

BIGGEST REGRET?

Taking the New North Road instead of the A640 and almost missing the birth of my son.

FONDEST MEMORY?

Just making it for the birth of my son — Daley Patrick Alfred Butcher. And meeting Carol. Carol Vivienne Butcher née Slogguth.

WORST TRAIT?

Now you probably don't know about this, petal, but there's a thing called 'mansplaining'.

ANY WORDS OF WISDOM?

There are two things in life that will never let you down. A dog and a bloody good constrictor knot.

Weapons and Militia

On, Wednesday 20th September, 1972

ILLUSTRATED CATALOGUE

(LOT 47)

PAIR OF MEDIEVAL BRASS-HILTED ARMING SWORDS

A rare pair of matching double-edged blades with cruciform hilts and ring pommels. 33-inch blades with ¾ length fuller, tapered cross-guard and pronounced écusson. Probably late 15th century.

Recorded provenance dating from 1584 when listed in the estate sale of 'Sir Humphrey Bone, late of Bone Hall' (now Button House). Certified copy of listing provided with lot.

Sold without scabbards, but including original Tudor pommel bolts and centre mount. (NB: centre mount is cracked and susceptible to load-bearing failure.)

NOTE: This is a decorative item. Misuse could result in injury.

This lot has no reserve.

7 March 1780

I am so tired I can hardly write but I simply must share the adventures of last night! Father took Eleanor and I to the Pleasure Gardens at Vauxhall. We have begged to be taken back ever since we first went with Mother when we were little girls and finally Father acquiesced to take us to a special ball given by the proprietor of the gardens. Thank you, thank you, thank you, Papa!

When we arrived, we saw that the main walkways were lit by a thousand lamps, with the colours of the flowers in bloom bursting out of the darkness like fireworks. Wonderfully dressed ladies and gentlemen everywhere you looked, music in the Chinese Pavilion and all sorts of gay entertainment.

When there was a pause in the music, Eleanor had the wonderful idea that we take one of the dark walks. Father was busy talking to one of his grey old merchant friends about boring things like 'trade' and 'taxation' so he wouldn't notice we were gone.

I followed Eleanor into the wilderness. There were many young people taking these walks, talking and laughing amongst themselves. It was like a special place where the normal rules did not apply. Well, I was so distracted and there were such windings and turnings on the path through the wilderness, I suddenly realised that Eleanor was almost out of view! I called for her to slow down but she mustn't have heard as she actually seemed to speed up her pace. I tried to run a little to get to her but I mustn't have been holding my skirt high enough as I somehow trapped it underfoot and tripped! I would surely have caused myself a terrible injury, not to mention great public embarrassment, were I not quite suddenly caught in the safe arms of a young gentleman.

For a moment, I was almost lying back in his arms, his face over mine, his eyes so kind and gentle. He helped me to my feet and inquired if I was all right. When I explained that I had lost my sister and that I feared I would not find my way out of the wilderness and back to the Pavilion, he offered to escort me. He said that he did not know the way himself but at least if we were to be lost, it would be together!

As we walked, we told each other about ourselves and found we had so much in common, both being fond of music and fashion and animals and parlour games and walking and talking and listening.

When we arrived back at the Pavilion, he introduced himself to Father. His name is Ernest Moore and Father said that he knew his parents and that he was welcome to call at the house. He said he would like to (I do hope he will!). He excused himself and left Father and I to enjoy the music. The orchestra began to play again and, quite suddenly, there were fireworks lighting up the sky above us! Actual fireworks this time, not flowers. I felt like they were all my own heart bursting with joy, all the colours of the rainbow.

Eventually Eleanor arrived, crying, and told us that she had been lost in the wilderness all that time. I feel terribly guilty about it because in truth, I'd quite forgotten about her. Poor sister. Still, we have a lot to look forward to this weekend. Lords Brummenbach and Pessenpugh are coming to see Father, so he will make sure we have a real feast! Who knows what I shall have to write about after that?

Part 1

9/8/83 · Part 1

Hola Mum!

Arrived safely after a delay on the tarmac at Gatwick. None other than Bergerac (John Nettles) was on board! He was very friendly and signed Carol's copy of Woman's Realm. I told him I expected a 'stinging rebuke' because of 'Nettles' but he just looked at me like I was ill. Torremolinos is much like Tossa De Mar except we don't know where anything is. Carol says, a change is as good as a rest. ('I'd find it more restful if I knew where to get a Twix and a Daily Mirror! TBC

Part 2 should have arrived too.

Mrs C. Butcher
22, McChesney Lane,
Almondbury, Huddersfield
HD4 7BJ   ENGLAND

No. 30 TORREMOLINOS
Playa de Carihuela

Ediciones Andalucia
Dep. Legal C. 9875-098

TARJETA POSTALE

2501 – TORREMOLINOS (Costa del Sol)

Part 2

Hola!

Even though we're unsure of the whereabouts of amenities, I must say the hotel swimming pool is superb and has two slides! One for the kids and a taller one for the dads. I went straight for the big gun. The Corkscrew! I forgot that you had to use a mat and was instantly thrown into a high-velocity spiral. I lost my speedos and Carol said I sounded like an ambulance siren! She threw me a towel so no one saw my crackerjacks. Tonight we're off to a restaurant to try Tortilla! Eggcellent! Love always, Patrick, Carol and Daley xxx

P.S 'Daley has sent you his own postcard x

Mrs C. Butcher
22, McChesney Lane,
Almondbury, Huddersfield
HD4 7BJ
ENGLAND

FOTOGRAFIA SOLEADA

ESPANA 3 PTAS CORREOS

Prohibida su Reproducción
Deposito Legal B 34345-XV

TORREMOLINOS Costa Del Sol

Dear grandma I'm
having a nice holiday!
I like the swimming
pool and the slide
and at night I have
chips and sossige and
lemonade. Daddy
Went down the
slide and his ~~trunks~~
trunks came o~~ff~~!
The man wouldn't
give them back!
Daddy is so funny!

I love you grandma! Daley xx

No9 Benalmadena
Playa Fuente de la Salud

FOTOGRAFÍA DE VACACIONES DE VERANO

Mrs E. Butcher

22, McChesney Lane,

Almondbury, Huddersfield,
HD4 7BJ
ENGLAND

Prohibida su Reproducción
Deposito Legal B 34345-XV

ESPANA
CORREOS

Portrait (partial) of Sir Humphrey Bone (1531-1575). Artist unknown. Woodworm damage to frame. Additional canvas missing, presumed lost.

HERE LYETH YE MORTAL REMAINS OF

SIR HUMPHREY
IGNATIUS BONE

WHO DEPARTED THIS EARTH
26 SEPTEMBER ANNO DOM. 1575
BY VIRTUE OF HIS HEAD BECOMING
MUCH SEP'RATE OF HIS BODY

ALAS, YE HEAD HATH BEEN MUCH
MISLAID BY MSSRS CORNELL & HYTNER
(UNDERTAKERS) WHOSE REGRETS WERE
HUMBLY CONVEYED TO YE FAMILY

SHOULD YE HEAD BE LOCAT'D, IT SHALT
BE INTERED HEREIN AT NO ADDITIONAL
COSTE, PLACED BETWIXT THE LEGS
IN SUCH A MANNER AS TO CAUSE
YE LEANEST DEGREE OF HUMILATION

WENDELL BOOKS

Dear Master Thorne,

First of all, how is your dear mother
Mrs Thorne? It is always a rare pleasure
to receive word from her. She really
is a keen champion of your writing,
as I'm sure you know, and was
most insistent that I read your latest
work. You must be so grateful for
her tireless advocacy!

I thank you for sending us the entire
manuscript of your poem 'Hermione &
Roger'. My goodness, what a heavy
document! I return it to you here to
save you the arduous task of copying
it out again should you decide to
write to any other publishers.

HERMIONE AND ROGER

a Poem by Thomas Thorne

Much has changed in the style of your
verse, I see, since I read your earlier
work 'A Volume of Short Verses Upon
the Nature of Desire'. I can see that
you took our comments to heart and
attempted something a little more
substantial. It really is exceptionally
long. If a poem's worth were measured
by the yard, you would find yourself
the rival to any man who ever raised
a quill! In fact, I cannot remember
ever having read a longer poem, or
certainly one that felt so long. I
suppose this is in part due to the
nature of the narrative form, which
progresses in a quite unfamiliar fashion.
One is so used to reading the traditional
style in which the writer takes his
reader through a sequence of related
events through time, perhaps through
the experiences of a central hero or
sometimes multiple characters connected
somehow by such events as transpire

around them. Here you have, perhaps deliberately (?) pioneered something altogether confoundingly different. Characters disappear, never to be heard from again (indeed, Hermione and Roger themselves are absent from forty-three verses), passages seem to take place years later (or earlier) and at one point the same sentence is repeated no less than twenty-nine times to torpefying effect.

Whilst I applaud your vivid sensory depictions, I did feel that perhaps too many lines were taken up with olfactory descriptions. At times the poem becomes rather a chronicle of of smells and, particularly in relation to the character of Hermione, I did begin to wonder if a more sensitive reader might feel a line of decency were rather being crossed.

I would also say that whilst metaphor is the surest weapon in the poet's armoury (if you'll forgive the metaphor), I do find that when an author employs one after the other so rapidly, so densely, often changing metaphors without warning mid-sentence, it can have a somewhat dizzying effect on the reader.

Those are my thoughts, for what they are worth. I am a fusty old man, no doubt, too set in the conventional way of things, and no doubt you will curse me for not appreciating your smashing of conventions, your bonfire of tradition! However, do not lose heart, if you do choose to take my counsel, let me say I am quite sure there is a poem in there <u>somewhere</u>.

Mathematically speaking, there <u>must</u> be. If one can weed out the mixed metaphors, non-sequiturs, irrelevances, repetitions, unseemly descriptions and narrative cul de sacs, it would at least be interesting to see what was left.

Yours most sincerely, and with warmest regards to your mother,

Mister Charles Wendell

Bookseller & Publisher

In the street

nder certain circumstances it may be necessary for a lady to go outside. On such occasions careful consideration must be paid to her dress and deportment as nowhere will she expose herself to such potential for public judgement or even ridicule.

A lady's dress must be immaculate in every detail, fitting perfectly, the sleeves and collars as white as freshly fallen snow, spotless boots, not a stitch out of place, all in service of the overall effect of not standing out in any way whatsoever. If you must wear a colour, let it be sober and, remember, only a person of very low birth indeed would introduce a *second* colour to her attire. Any such decorative frivolities as ribbons and so on will certainly mark you out as a person of loose morals. Fashion is for the vulgar, a well-bred lady is above such things. (As a side note on dress, a lady's corset should be always tightened to its fullest possible capacity. Being short of breath is often a sign that you are speaking more than is wholly appropriate.)

A lady may take the arm of her husband, father or, if he is of impeccable reputation, brother. *She must not touch any other man in public* unless he is offering her his hand to descend from her carriage or omnibus. In such circumstances one must thank the man, bow and depart without further comment.

If a lady sees a friend, male or female, with whom she wishes to speak, they can join her as she walks, but she should *never stop to talk* to them. We cannot have people idly standing about the streets, chattering. This is not France! If you must hold a conversation (as you walk), take care not to speak any louder than is absolutely necessary to be clear. If you enunciate your consonants crisply, you will find that very little projection is required at all.

Never laugh in the street. If your companion says something excessively amusing, indicate your appreciation with a polite smile. If you cannot contain yourself, be sure to laugh in a gentle humming fashion, lips closed and pursed – 'Hmm hmm hmm.' A lady who opens her mouth to laugh in the street invites scandal.

A lady must never turn her head more than 45 degrees and only then if absolutely necessary, to acknowledge the remark of a gentleman companion. Otherwise, she must always face forward. Never look down at the floor, you are not a servant! Neither should you turn your face to the heavens, you are not in prayer!

Do not slouch or drag your feet like a surly petulant child. Instead, always maintain a lady-like erection. Hold your parasol in one hand and your dress up a little with the other but under no circumstances should you allow your ankle to be exposed. If the dress must be soiled, so be it. Manure can be washed off a hem but a reputation as a wanton harlot will not be scrubbed away so easily. For this reason, one must avoid being outdoors in high winds, it is simply not worth the risk that a gust may billow one's skirts and expose an ankle, or worse, both ankles. Only prostitutes would venture out in a storm.

𝔚𝔥𝔢𝔫 𝔱𝔯𝔞𝔳𝔢𝔩𝔩𝔦𝔫𝔤

lady's aspect and decorum are seldom more tested than in travel. If, for example, she can maintain a ladylike demeanour in the act of stepping from a jetty to a rowing boat, then she will find most other settings a walk in the park (though do read 'When Walking in the Park' for specific instructions on respectable conduct in that particular setting). Advance planning is

"There is nothing
– nothing – that
cannot be lied about."

JULIAN

NAME JULIAN

WHERE WERE YOU BORN?

People think I was born with a silver spoon in my mouth, but far from it. My mother gave birth to me at our modest holiday home in the tiny village of Tillington, West Sussex. My mother was a humble greengrocer's daughter. Yes, he had a national chain of stores that went on to become Britain's largest supermarket brand, but he always remained a simple grocer at heart. There were complications at my birth (my head was too big apparently) but thankfully my father, a humble ear and nose surgeon at London's largest private hospital called upon the services of a dozen or so maternity staff to help. I eventually emerged, silent-screaming and trying to catch my breath.

HOW DID YOU DIE?

No comment. But let's just say I left life in a not dissimilar way to how I entered it.

FAVOURITE FOOD?

A seafood platter? Is that cheating? I like my platters cold. I'm talking lobster, crab, prawn, oysters, clams, razor clams, whelks, crayfish, octopus. All washed down with a chilled, flinty Sancerre — failing that a Pouilly-Fumé, failing that Chablis, failing that Sauvignon Blanc (New Zealand only!), failing that a Chenin Blanc, failing that Viognier, failing that just house plonk I suppose, I'm not too fussy.

FAVOURITE DRINK?

For seafood, see above. For red meats it has to be Cabernet Sauvignon. Australian or an American Napa Valley. I'm talking full-bodied. Think Ann Widdecombe NOT Edwina Currie! (Snorts odiously.) For mornings you can't beat a mimosa. Late evenings very cold Scotch. And if I'm driving just a few cold cans of lager.

FAVOURITE SONG?

Peter Cetera — 'Glory of Love'. I think it just says everything you need to know about me: a hero who will fight for your honour for the glory of love. Of course the line about living forever should be taken with a pinch of salt, but the rest is bang on.

FAVOURITE SPORT?

Got to be golf. Some call it a good walk spoilt; I call it a good walk IMPROVED. Yes, it takes up a lot of green space, but what a sport. MAN vs THELAND!

BIGGEST REGRET?

Hmmm. Lot to choose from here. Putting personal regrets aside for a moment, I'd say I regret campaigning to join the EEC the most. I mean 'Made in Britain' is a globally recognised hallmark of quality. I can only imagine the prosperity we'd be enjoying by now if we'd have stuck to our guns and stayed out of Europe. Why, we'd be the envy of the civilised world. But I suppose we're stuck with it now. I mean, no one's going to open that can of worms again, are they?

FONDEST MEMORY?

I have to say my wedding or the day my daughter Rachel was born... but in reality it was the day I picked six winners in the placepot at Ascot. I won't say how much I won, but I took everyone in my corporate box to Morocco for a week — and nearly missed my wedding day! (Snorts again, stifled laughter, then sadness.)

WORST TRAIT?

My honesty.

ANY WORDS OF WISDOM?

Never get caught with your trousers down.

BOYS ADVENTURE CLUB

READING 4th
NEWSLETTER

Sunday 6th August 1983

A TRIP TO THE SEASIDE

DATES FOR YOUR DIARY:

Tues Sept 6th . . . .
ANNUAL CAKE-BAKE-BY-THE-LAKE
(Will actually be held in the hut
this year, following last year's
incident)

Tues Sept 27th . . . .
GOOD DEED DAY
A chance to earn your Helping
Hands badge!

Oct 27th – Nov 4th . . . .
PENNY FOR THE GUY WEEK
All proceeds (fittingly) going
towards Guy's operation.

Sat Nov 5th . . . .
BONNE FIRE
In partnership with the French
Exchange club

Fri Nov 25th . . . .
THE QUEEN-QUEEN DANCE
Celebrating Her Majesty's 30th
year on the throne with the music
of Freddie Mercury

Sat Dec 10th . . . .
CHRISTMAS FAIR
Gifts for the eyes (craft), mouth
(cake) and ears (carols)

Fri Dec 23rd . . . .
CAROLS BY CANDLELIGHT
(not by candlelight)

Hello!

Last Saturday was our annual
trip to the seaside and what an
eventful day it was!

We got on the road around 8am and
spirits were high. We all had a
jolly singalong to the excellent
cassette compilation Martin
Patterson had made, featuring
Black Lace, the Quo and a group
I'd never heard before called
Madonna. Martin insisted we listen
to it on a loop for the entire
journey. Only seven songs in
total, so quite a lot of rewinding,
but at least we're all well
accustomed to the lyrics now.

We made good progress down
the A283 and before long, we'd
arrived at sunny Littlehampton.
(With just 11 boys travel sick! A
massive improvement on last year.)
We alighted the coach and made
our way down to the seafront.
First up, the pier!

Some of the boys had brought
their own crabbing lines so we
headed to the end of the pier to
have a go. We then realised we
didn't have any bait, luckily my
volunteer assistant and driver
John Chidsey said he had a nifty
idea and disappeared. Poor John
must have searched the whole
of Littlehampton because he was
gone for ages but he finally
tottered back with a load of pork

scratchings, he said he got them
from a quaint little shop called
The Ship. Well the crabs went mad
for them! Before long we had so
many crabs we could have ditched
our sandwiches and made a fruit
de mer! (That's French.) The
boys were so keen to catch crabs
that soon we were overrun! One
lad had one pinched on his nose,
another had one down his shorts,
an elderly lady sat near us found
a crab in her purse and passed
out. Heaven knows how it got in
there! Ah we did laugh (they did).
We said goodbye to our catch and
threw them back into the sea,
some boys impressively so.

After our sandwiches we headed
to the amusements where the lads
were free to spend their pocket
money on Pac-Man and the 2p
pushers. Big Tony Clemence won 20
pound on a gambling machine. (Mr
and Mrs Clemence, FYI, normally
I wouldn't advocate a 14 year old
playing a gambling machine but 20
quid can't be sniffed at and it's
great to see the scale of the lad
really coming into its own. No one
even looked twice.)

After some persuasion by the
boys, I reluctantly partook in a
palm read by Miss Gypsy Flanagan.
She grasped my hand and carefully
studied the creases and lines.
She told me to 'beware of a true
companion' and warned me of a
'great pain in the neck'.

BOYS ADVENTURE CLUB

What? My mother-in-law?!

But honestly readers, what a load of codswallop.

Speaking of cod it was nearly time for everyone's favourite bit (certainly mine), fish and chips on the beach! My assistant and driver John volunteered to get it and the queue must have been enormous because poor John was gone for ages again. That didn't matter though, we went down to the sands and worked up an appetite playing French cricket (that's French). Soon, through the haze, we saw John shuffling towards us with two big bags of God's own scran under his armpits. Delicious!

There were so many chips left over the boys started feeding the seagulls. When I was on the pay telescope the little blighters sneaked up behind me and put chips in my pockets and the turn-ups on my shorts. Before long I was swarmed by the frenzied creatures. Swooping in like Stukas and pecking at my nethers! The boys were having a right old laugh as I created a mobile baitball! I had no choice but to leg it into the sea, all the way until my head was completely submerged. I then held my breath and waited for the birds to cease and disperse. I suppose that's one way to work off your fish and chips!

Sadly though, it was time to go, so we all trundled (and I squelched) up to the car park for the final roll call. 'Hang on?' I thought. Someone's missing! It was none other than my assistant and driver John. We'd left him on the beach! We walked back only to find him fast asleep in a deck

chair. (Turns out he'd had a few, so muggins here had to drive home!) We wound our way back to Reading singing those seven songs we all know so, so well, while I dried my cash on the blow heater.

By the time we got to Chiddingfold, I noticed everyone was asleep. I gently switched off the music and, interlaced with the grunts of my assistant and 'driver' John, all I could hear was the tiny satisfied snores of the younguns. I sat there in my

still-damp clothes and thought 'this is living'!

On the whole a very memorable day. A real attack on the senses. Here's to next year!

Yours sincerely,

Pat Butcher

CLUB LEADER
READING 4TH.

Telegram 1

POST OFFICE TELEGRAM

Charges to pay ___ s. ___ d. RECEIVED

OFFICE STAMP

Prefix. Time handed in. Office of Origin and Service Instructions. Words.

HERTFORDSHIRE 3RD JUNE 1940

At ___ m From HQ 3 Coy (Int.) (857432) By ___

At ___ m To GENERAL FISHER (SOUTHERN COMMAND) By ___

URGENT CONFIDENTIAL PRIORITY

GENERAL STOP URGENT REQUEST FOR MUNITIONS AT HQ 3 COY (INT.) STOP REQUEST FOR SMALL ARMS TO DEFEND PERIMETER FROM GERMAN ADVANCE STOP JERRY IS LIKELY TO ATTACK STOP LEE ENFIELD MK 2 (20?) STOP WEBLEY MK IV SERVICE REVOLVER (3?) STOP.

For free repetition of do[ubtful words] at office of delivery. Othe[r]

Telegram 2

POST OFFICE TELEGRAM

Charges to pay ___ s. ___ d. RECEIVED

OFFICE STAMP

Prefix. Time handed in. Office of Origin and Service Instructions. Words.

WILTSHIRE 4TH JUNE

At ___ m From CAPT. O CHATTERTON-PILLAR By ___

At ___ m To OFFICER COMMANDING (HQ 3 COY (INT.)) By ___

++++CONFIDENTIAL++++

PRIORITY STOP NO MATTER WHAT YOU SEND TO THE GENERAL IT WILL BE MY OFFICE THAT REPLIES STOP SHOULD YOU =PERSIST I WILL TAKE FURTHER DISCIPLINARY ACTION STOP THIS MATTER IS NOW CLOSED STOP

+ TS 0

[ENQ]UIRY " or call, with this form [...] n, and, if possible, the envelope. B or C

Telegram 3

POST OFFICE TELEGRAM

Charges to pay PM ___ 15 d. RECEIVED

OFFICE STAMP

Prefix. Time handed in. Office of Origin and Service Instructions. Words.

29

HEREFORDSHIRE 5TH JUNE 1940

TS

At ___ m From HQ 3 Coy (Int.) (857432)

At ___ m To CAPT. O CHATTERTON-PILLAR

URGENT

CAPTAIN STOP AT LEAST ISSUE ME WITH A SIDEARM STOP = THE STAFF HERE WILL BE RELIEVED IF THEIR C/O IS PREPARED STOP.

For free repetition of doubtful words telephone "TELEGRAMS ENQUIRY " or call, with this form at office of delivery. Other enquiries should be accompanied by this form, and, if possible, the envelope.

POST  OFFICE
TELEGRAM

Charges to pay

____ s. ____ d.

RECEIVED

No. ____

OFFICE STAMP

Prefix. Time handed in. Office of Origin and Service Instructions. Words.

WILTSHIRE 7TH JUNE TELEGRAMS (office stamp)

At ____ m
From CAPT. O CHATTERTON-PILLAR
By ____

At ____ m
To OFFICER COMMANDING (HQ 3 COY (INT))
By ____

++++CONFIDENTIAL++++

PRIORITY STOP YOU WILL CEASE THIS OR
I WILL ISSUE COURT MARTIAL STOP

For free repetition of d...
at office of delivery. Oth...

POST OFFICE
TELEGRAM

Charges to pay

____ s. ____ d.

RECEIVED

No. 668

OFFICE STAMP

HEREFORDSHIRE 3RD JUNE 1940 (office stamp)

Prefix **26** Time handed in. Office of Origin and Service Instructions. Words.

At ____ m
From HQ 3 Coy (Int.) (857432)
By ____

At ____ m
To CAPT. O CHATTERTON-PILLAR
By ____

URGENT*

PLEASE STOP

For free repetition of doubtful words telephone "TELEGRAMS ENQUIRY" or call, with this form
at office of delivery. Other enquiries should be accompanied by this form and ... te, the envelope

---

POST OFFICE
TELEGRAM

Charges to pay

PM9 s. 15 d.

RECEIVED

No. 31

OFFICE STAMP

WILTSHIRE 7TH JUNE TELEGRAMS (office stamp)

Prefix. Time handed in. Office of Origin and Service Instructions. Words.

MS

At ____ m
From CAPT. O. CHATTERTON-PILLAR
By ____

At ____ m
To OFFICER COMMANDING (HQ 3 COY (INT))
By ____

NO STOP NOW STOP STOP

For free repetition of doubtful words telephone "TELEGRAMS ENQUIRY" or call, with this form
at office of delivery. Other enquiries should be accompanied by this form, and, if possible, the envelope

أوفيس أف ممر محمد أبو ومنير الجدف

+++++++ CONFIDENTIAL +++++++

15th April 1989

Salam alekum wa ramatula wa barakatu

Dear Mr Julian Fawcett MP,

It was a great pleasure to meet you in London as part of our last trade
delegation to your wonderful city. Times are uncertain for our country and we
welcome your kindness.

I would like to thank you and the staff of Baubles Nightclub in Chelsea for a
wonderful evening. Myself and the trade delegation were greatly entertained by
your friends. I wish to thank also the dancers Cheryl and Krystal. Such energy!

Indeed **Mr Fawcett** we enjoyed our stay at your house The Brambles at the weekend.
What a magnificent home you have.

We discussed your interest, Mr Fawcett, in providing for us certain 'pipe
equipment' and 'computer systems' to work the 'pipe equipment'. You mention to me
several times you can talk to the right people in your country to provide such
technology? We also take great interest in the 'tanks for storage' that you talk
of. The pipes and the tanks are what we seek.

We would look very favourably on such a special deal and we know that you have
great expenses. Your swimming pool we know is costly to heat and your wife is
very happy to have a new orangery, I think.

Perhaps you would like to discuss these arrangements at our palace here in
Tripoli? A special flight can be arranged and we would entertain you at the
presidential beach resort. A holiday for you and your family? Why not? You work
so hard in your parliament.

I hope that you can persuade your friends to help supply this equipment. Great
fortunes await you sir.

My sincerest thanks to you and your great country.

May God bless you.

Yassin Bint Abu Talib Deputy Aide to Col. Al-Gadaffi.
Chambers of Commerce,
P.O. Box 2321. Tripoli, LIBYA
(218) 22-33754

الغرف التجارية
ص. طرابلس، ليبيا 2321
(218) 22-33754

From: mikecooper@buttonhouse.com
Subject: Soz
Date: 17 August 2023 at 05:50
To: margot.fawcett@thehomegnome.com

MF

dear margot, surprise. it's me, julian. don't worry i am dead. i didn't fake my death or do a lord lucan. although maybe that would have been better for you, i don't know. i found your email on the home gnome website. good to see you're still volunteering. remember to claim back tax on all your expenses though; travel, lunches etc. it all adds up. i wrote that so you'll know it really is me.

goodness margot this is such a hard letter to write. not just because of the way i popped my clogs (apols, more on that later) but because i can only press one key at a time as i am a ghost. it takes great effort and a looooooong time. i've been writing this for 2 hours already. in hindsight i should be more sparing to save my finger - which gets v achy - probly shouldn't have done the lord lucan bit for example. or this bit…..

it been 4 hours now since i wrote last bit cus robin caused a power cut n alison - who can see me - had to perform a 'recovery' on mike's - he can't see me - laptop. robin such an idiot sumtimes. also he a caveman - long story . finger so achy now. i keep brief. apols.

so, mainly margs, reason for email this, sorry. just apols all round. pols big time. affair with sec only been going 2 years i proms. so, actually was after yr tryst with tennis coach, so…. no excuses tho. my bad. if any consolation i ghost with no trousers 4 eternity now which mega embaz i can tell u. soz. finger so ouchy. got 2 rest nw.

that's better. anyway, i should prob not take up more of yr time. hope you have moved on. tennis coach? anyhoo, apols again bout headlines n stuff after i snuffed. british press tossers.

hope rachel ok. she so beautals, like u. Is she in green party. good for her. i hear planet hot because of cows now. who knew. good 4 her. dead proud - no pun intend.

ok, best go now it get v late. ghost need sleep too. who knew. would kill 4 pyjamas. well, not kill but… amazing things u take 4 granted. ok i waffle now. shush lips.

to end i wan say, im bad man but i luvd you darling curly bun, from bottom o my non beating heart. prob wont write again. too emosh and finger totes broken. lol.

yours in luv
jj-plums

ps. left v nice rolex watch in garage under freezer in marks n spncr bag. was gift from saddam hussein. hid during gulf war 1 when he went bad. forgot bout it but prob wrth few bob now.
pps. put a bet on arthurs cross in grand nash. lots time to study form and it shoo in. gud luck. x

List of Contents